The clinical scenarios described in this book are entirely fictional. No resemblance to real people or actual cases is intended.

Every effort was made to ensure the accuracy of the material presented in this book at the time of publication.

Given that policies, procedures, and instructions can change at any time, candidates should always read and follow directions provided by the registering/licensing authority, the presiding officer, and the instructions contained in the Nurse Registration/Licensure Examination.

Candidates use the information, materials, and suggestions in this book at their own risk. Neither the Canadian Nurses Association nor its Testing Division assumes any responsibility for candidates' performance on the Nurse Registration/Licensure Examination.

2nd printing, January 1998

**ISBN 1-55119-132-6. 2ND EDITION, 1995
(ISBN 0-88879-036-8. 1ST EDITION, 1992)**

Printed in Canada

TABLE OF CONTENTS

PREFACE

Congratulations! You have just purchased *The Canadian RN Exam Prep Guide*, published by the Canadian Nurses Association (CNA) to help you prepare for the Nurse Registration/Licensure Examination (RN Exam) used in Canada. This second edition of the guide is specially designed to familiarize you with a new series of examinations that will be introduced in August 1995.

The Canadian RN Exam Prep Guide is the only prep guide available that is created by the CNA Testing Division—the same group that develops and administers the RN Exam across Canada. The knowledge and expertise of the professionals in this group make them the best qualified to produce an RN Exam prep guide.

CNA's *Prep Guide* has proven to be both useful and popular. The first edition, released in November 1992, has sold more than 14,000 copies. In that edition, we asked students to tell us how we could improve the book. They responded and we've listened. This edition is substantially different from the first, not only because it is based on the new series of examinations, but also because it has been modified to better meet your needs. For example, we've improved the binding to make the guide more convenient to use, and we've included a list of abbreviations that appear in the exam. We've revised the format and content of the *Prep Guide* to make it as useful and user-friendly as possible. Please send us your comments and suggestions about this all-new edition on the Satisfaction Survey included at the back of the book.

CNA's *Prep Guide* is available in both English and French. We suggest that you select the guide which corresponds to the language of the exam you plan to write.

The CNA Board of Directors and the staff in Testing Division would like to thank the many nurses who contributed to this edition of the *Prep Guide*. As a result of their efforts, we are confident that this guide will be of great assistance to you as you prepare to write your examination.

In conclusion, my colleagues and I wish you success in writing the RN Exam and throughout your nursing career.

G. Budgell

Glen R. Budgell, Ph.D.
Director of Testing
Canadian Nurses Association

ACKNOWLEDGMENTS

The following people generously gave their time and expertise to the creation of *The Canadian RN Exam Prep Guide* (2nd ed.).

EXAM REVIEW PANEL

This panel consisted of five nurses from different locations and work settings in Canada. They reviewed the content of the Practice Exam and rationales—independently and as a group—to ensure the quality of these important *Prep Guide* components.

Helen Babouras
Vanier College
St-Laurent, PQ

Diane Pagan
Sudbury General Hospital
Sudbury, ON

Norma Price
Victoria General Hospital
School of Nursing
Halifax, NS

Karen Ryall
B.C.'s Children's Hospital
Vancouver, BC

Patrice Yamada
Grace General Hospital
School of Nursing
Winnipeg, MB

NURSE ITEM WRITERS

The following nurses participated in item-writing sessions, conducted in the fall of 1993, at which questions and rationales were developed for the Practice Exam.

Lynda Aikenhead
Health Sciences Centre
School of Nursing
Winnipeg, MB

Christine Ateah
University of Manitoba
Faculty of Nursing
Winnipeg, MB

Helen Babouras
Vanier College
St-Laurent, PQ

Mona Baryluk
Cape Breton Regional Hospital
School of Nursing
Sydney, NS

Melanie Basso
Vancouver Community College
Vancouver, BC

Jean Bergman
Fanshawe College
London, ON

Myrtle Blinn
Heritage College
Hull, PQ

Lowleen Coles
Prince Edward Island School
of Nursing
Charlottetown, PE

Sheila Cross
Vanier College
St-Laurent, PQ

Rose Cunha
Humber College of Applied Arts
and Technology
Etobicoke, ON

Mary-Lou Ellerton
Dalhousie University
School of Nursing
Halifax, NS

Hether Fankhauser
Dawson College
Westmount, PQ

Diane Harrison
Saskatchewan Institute of
Applied Science and Technology
Regina, SK

Martha Horsburgh
University of Windsor
School of Nursing
Windsor, ON

Phyllis Kerr
Bathurst School of Nursing
Bathurst, NB

Marian Landry
Niagara College of Applied Arts
and Technology
St. Catharines, ON

Angèla LeBlanc
The Miss A. J. MacMaster
School of Nursing
Moncton, NB

Isla Marsh
Grace General Hospital
School of Nursing
Winnipeg, MB

Mary Jean McCarthy
University of Prince Edward
Island School of Nursing
Charlottetown, PE

Janet McKnight
McMaster University
School of Nursing
Hamilton, ON

Susan Mussell
Health Sciences Centre
Winnipeg, MB

Alice Noftall
Grace General Hospital
School of Nursing
St. John's, NF

Elizabeth O'Driscoll
St. Clares Mercy Hospital
School of Nursing
St. John's, NF

Diane Pagan
Sudbury General Hospital
Sudbury, ON

Diana Pallen
Lakehead University
School of Nursing
Thunder Bay, ON

Cindy Peternelj-Taylor
University of Saskatchewan
College of Nursing
Saskatoon, SK

Norma Price
Victoria General Hospital
School of Nursing
Halifax, NS

Janet Rankin
Malaspina College
Nanaimo, BC

Karen Ryall
B.C.'s Children's Hospital
Vancouver, BC

Sandra Sadler
Health Sciences Centre
School of Nursing
Winnipeg, MB

Margaret Swedish
Grant MacEwan Community
College
Edmonton, AB

Lois Tessier
Red River Community College
Winnipeg, MB

Carmelita Tolentino
Health Sciences Centre
School of Nursing
Winnipeg, MB

Deborah Vandewater
Camp Hill Medical Centre
Halifax, NS

Patrice Yamada
Grace General Hospital
School of Nursing
Winnipeg, MB

CNA STAFF

A number of CNA staff members contributed, in different ways, to the creation of *The Canadian RN Exam Prep Guide* (2nd ed.). These people included the eight members of the "Core Team" who were responsible for planning and managing all of the activities related to the development of the *Prep Guide*, along with several individuals who were asked to assist with specific aspects of the project.

Core Team
Maryse Céré
Martine Devaux
Christiane Fradet
Johanne Killeen
Hugh Malcolm
Nadine Mathieu
Michael Stein
Susan Ward

Staff Contributors
Françoise Boutet
John Braham
Carole Dazé
Amanda Joab
Leslie Johnston
Josée Larivière-Asselin
Janice Newman-White
Barbara Sibbald
Diane St-Pierre

CHAPTER

1

Using this Guide

INTRODUCTION

The Canadian RN Exam Prep Guide (2nd ed.) has been developed by the Canadian Nurses Association (CNA) Testing Division to assist candidates who will be writing the Nurse Registration/Licensure Examination (RN Exam). This second edition of the *Prep Guide* is designed specifically for those candidates who plan to write the new series of examinations being introduced in August 1995.

Success on the RN Exam depends on two main factors: (1) your knowledge of nursing principles and content, and (2) your ability to apply this knowledge, in the context of specific health care scenarios, on the RN Exam.

This guide can help you in both areas. Completing the *Prep Guide* Practice Exam will help you review and integrate the concepts you have learned in your nursing program; it will also help you assess your skill in applying that knowledge. The test instructions, test-taking strategies and sample response sheets can be used to enhance your readiness to write the RN Exam. What better way to get ready than to gain practical experience by trying the practice questions in the *Prep Guide* and knowing what to expect on the RN Exam!

The *Prep Guide* consists of several chapters designed to help you with different aspects of your preparation. In this chapter, you will learn the best way to use the *Prep Guide*, given your individual needs and the amount of time you have to prepare for the

RN Exam. Chapter 2 provides you with background information on the development, organization, and format of the RN Exam. Chapter 3 contains a variety of general test-taking strategies, as well as specific strategies for answering multiple-choice questions. The Practice Exam is presented in Chapter 4. Chapter 5 explains how to use the answer keys to score the Practice Exam, and describes how the actual RN Exam is scored.

After checking your score on the Practice Exam against a score interpretation scale, you may wish to develop a Performance Profile—a self-evaluation of your strengths and weaknesses. Chapter 6 shows you how to create your Performance Profile. The rationales for each option in the Practice Exam are found in Chapter 7.

The Bibliography lists all the references cited in the question rationales. Appendix A presents the list of competencies that make up the content domain for the RN Exam. Addresses of the provincial and territorial registering/licensing authorities are provided in Appendix B. And Appendix C contains a list of common abbreviations that appear on the RN Exam. At the back of the *Prep Guide*, you will find two blank response sheets for the Practice Exam, and a Satisfaction Survey. Your opinion is important to us and we encourage you to send us your feedback so we may improve future editions of *The Canadian RN Exam Prep Guide*.

BEFORE YOU BEGIN...

The *Prep Guide* is designed to familiarize you with the format of the actual exam and to provide you with information on the content of the exam. The Practice Exam contained in this book is a simulation of an actual RN Exam. There are 258 questions in the Practice Exam (two exam books, each containing 129 questions).

The questions presented in the Practice Exam are typical of those you will see on the RN Exam. They represent common and predictable health situations of the population in those contexts or environments where beginning practitioners would work in a generalist role. As with the actual RN Exam, the questions on the Practice Exam have been developed and reviewed by nurses who represent a variety of nursing programs, different clinical backgrounds, and different regions of the country. Furthermore, the Practice Exam has been designed according to the specifications and guidelines outlined in the *Blueprint for the Criterion-Referenced Nurse Registration/ Licensure Examination* (1993), the document used to construct the actual RN Exam. Hence, although the Practice Exam is not identical to the RN Exam that you will write, both exams contain questions that measure specific competencies expected of nurses beginning to practice.

One of the most important features of the *Prep Guide* is that, for each question on the Practice Exam, rationales are provided to explain why the options are correct or incorrect. These rationales emphasize nursing concepts and principles that are essential for beginning practitioners. For example, although the pharmacology questions and the communication questions on the *Prep Guide* Practice Exam are different from those on the actual exam, the general principles being tested are the same, because the questions are developed from the same set of competencies. Thus, by using the Practice Exam to review and reinforce the principles of safe administration of drugs and therapeutic communication, you will be better prepared to answer these types of questions on the RN Exam.

It is important to note that, although your score on the Practice Exam can give you some indication of how prepared you are for the RN Exam, the *Prep Guide* is only one aid to promote your success. The *Prep Guide* should be used to supplement and reinforce the knowledge and skills taught in your educational program.

Each question on the *Prep Guide* Practice Exam is supported by two references. Most of these references have been published within the past 5 years. The purpose of the references is twofold: to indicate that the correct answer within each of the questions has authoritative support from at least two experts in the field; and to provide you with a source for further reading and review. Every attempt has been made to use references that are up-to-date, accessible, and accepted within the nursing community. If you are unable to locate the specific references cited in the Bibliography, there are many other equally sound nursing texts that provide support for the questions in the Practice Exam.

METHODS OF USING THE *PREP GUIDE*

The *Prep Guide* can be used in different ways, depending on your particular needs and the amount of time you have before you write the RN Exam. The three methods suggested below are not independent, but can actually be used successively as part of a comprehensive study plan. Each method should be preceded by a review of Chapters 1, 2, and 3 before advancing to Chapter 4, *Taking the Practice Exam.* The three methods differ in approach, based on the amount of time you have available before you write the RN Exam. They cover periods of several months prior, one month prior, and two weeks prior to the actual exam.

METHOD A:
IF YOU HAVE SEVERAL MONTHS BEFORE WRITING THE RN EXAM

If you have several months before the exam, you may wish to write the complete Practice Exam under conditions that do not simulate the actual exam (e.g., do not be concerned with time limits; look ahead to a rationale to understand why a given answer is correct, before choosing your answer). Consider this process as a "dry run" to familiarize yourself with the *Prep Guide* and the format and layout of the exam. In using this approach, work question-by-question without using the response sheets. Answer one question and immediately check whether you selected the correct answer. Then read the rationales for the correct answer and the incorrect options, to gain insight into what made you answer correctly or incorrectly.

This method will give you hands-on experience with multiple-choice questions, and help you identify any difficulties you may have with the multiple-choice format (e.g., not picking up on key words in the question, making unwarranted assumptions and reading too much into questions). On page 23 you will find a Checklist of Common Test-Taking Errors that will help you determine if you have particular difficulties with multiple-choice questions that you can correct before writing the exam.

Since this method does not simulate actual exam conditions, we recommend that you do not calculate your total score or make any inferences based on that score.

METHOD B:
IF YOU HAVE ONE MONTH BEFORE WRITING THE RN EXAM

If you have approximately one month before the exam, you will want to more closely simulate actual exam conditions, and still take advantage of a considerable amount of time in which to address any self-diagnosed weaknesses. With this method, complete the Practice Exam, either in its entirety or in discrete sections (e.g., a set of cases, a set of independent questions, or one exam book) before checking your answers against the answer key. Next, calculate your total score and interpret it according to the guidelines provided in Chapter 5. Then develop your Performance Profile, to identify your strengths and weaknesses (see Chapter 6).

The results of this self-diagnosis can then be used to identify gaps or deficiencies in your knowledge and skills. By knowing that you are weak in particular competency categories or nursing practice categories, you can make your remaining study time more productive by concentrating on those specific areas. Studying for the RN Exam will also be made easier by consulting the reference books linked to specific topics in nursing. You will find these references cited with the rationales for each question, and listed in full in the Bibliography.

METHOD C:
IF YOU HAVE TWO WEEKS
BEFORE WRITING THE RN EXAM

Method C is based upon a complete simulation of the actual exam. Follow the Practice Exam instructions precisely, time yourself, and use the response sheets, as if you were actually writing the RN Exam. You can still benefit from creating your Performance Profile, as suggested in Method B. For the remaining study time, it may be most useful for you to concentrate on specific areas in which any weaknesses were identified. When using Method C, if you do not have time to obtain the references that correspond to your areas of weakness, you may prefer to concentrate on the rationales provided for each question in the Practice Exam.

CHAPTER

2

Background on
the RN Exam

BACKGROUND ON THE RN EXAM

Each province and territory in Canada is responsible for ensuring that all nurses within its jurisdiction meet an acceptable level of competence before they begin to practice. This level of competence is measured by the Nurse Registration/Licensure Exam administered by all provincial/territorial registering/licensing authorities.* This ensures a common standard that all nurses in Canada must meet.

The Canadian Nurses Association Testing (CNAT) division has been developing the RN Exam since 1970. (Before that, jurisdictions made their own arrangements for testing, and most used exams developed in the United States.) Originally, each exam book represented a discrete clinical area (e.g., medicine, surgery, pediatrics, etc.); since August 1980, however, the exam content has been integrated to make the exam comprehensive in nature. That is, the material from areas such as pharmacology, nutrition, growth and development, etc., is incorporated into a variety of health care situations that a nurse entering practice, as a generalist, is most likely to encounter.

In 1993, CNAT introduced another significant change to the process used to develop the RN Exam. At that time, the process was changed from a *norm-referenced* approach to a *criterion-referenced* approach. With the criterion-referenced approach, the RN Exam is developed to measure an explicitly defined content domain, which consists of the competencies expected of nurses beginning to practice. These competencies, and the guidelines and specifications that outline the way they should be measured on the exam, are presented in the CNA's *Blueprint for the Criterion-Referenced Nurse Registration/Licensure Examination* (1993). Criterion-referenced RN Exam writing sessions begin in August 1995.

As with the previous exam, the new version of the RN Exam is the end result of many test development activities that take place throughout a 2-year period. Nurse educators, clinicians, and administrators from across Canada create and evaluate exam questions with assistance from CNAT test consultants who ensure that the RN Exam meets the *Blueprint* guidelines and specifications.

* The registering/licensing authorities impose eligibility criteria, such as the completion of an approved program of nursing education, which provide the added information required to decide on an individual's readiness to practice nursing.

WHAT IS TESTED WITH THE RN EXAM

As mentioned earlier, the content and specifications for the RN Exam are described in the *Blueprint*. A Summary Chart that outlines the *Blueprint* specifications for exam development is presented on page 11 for your reference. And, in Appendix A, you will find the complete list of 238 competencies that make up the content domain for the RN Exam. Each question on the RN Exam is linked to one of these competencies. The sections below provide brief explanations of the variables and guidelines referred to in the Summary Chart.

COMPETENCIES

This first section of the Summary Chart shows that the list of competencies has been divided into four groups, and that each group receives a different weight on the RN Exam. The groups were formed on the basis of a competency validation survey, in which nurses across Canada rated the competencies according to importance, frequency, and difficulty. The weights associated with these groups have been assigned to reflect the relative importance, frequency, and difficulty of the competencies in each group. Thus, competencies from Group A (high importance/frequency/difficulty) will have the highest representation on the RN Exam, while those from Group D (relatively low importance/frequency/difficulty) will have the lowest representation. (Note that the list of competencies in Appendix A has been divided into these four groups and the weighting of each group on the RN Exam has been indicated.)

STRUCTURAL VARIABLES

The general structure and appearance of the RN Exam are determined by the following structural variables:

Examination Length and Format
The RN Exam consists of 240 to 260 multiple-choice questions.

Test Equating
To ensure the equivalency of different versions of the RN Exam (e.g., French and English versions, or same-language versions administered at different times), a predetermined set of questions, known as anchor items, appears on all exam versions.

Item Presentation
Approximately half of the questions on the RN Exam are presented in a *case-based* format; i.e., a group of approximately five questions that are associated with a brief introductory text. The remainder of the exam consists of *independent questions,* which are stand-alone questions not associated with the cases or other questions on the exam.

TAXONOMIES: COGNITIVE AND AFFECTIVE DOMAINS

Questions on the RN Exam measure candidates' knowledge and abilities in nursing content across different levels of the *cognitive* domain. The three levels of cognitive ability reflected in the RN Exam are: Knowledge/Comprehension, Application, and Critical Thinking. As well, certain questions on the exam are designed to measure aspects of the *affective* domain. The cognitive and affective domains are defined below.

The Cognitive Domain
Knowledge/Comprehension refers to those mental abilities used when you recall and understand certain definitions, facts, or principles. For example, a sound base of nursing knowledge is required for you to know common side effects of a certain medication and to understand your client's physiological reactions to it. Knowledge/Comprehension questions make up 25 to 35% of the RN Exam.

SUMMARY CHART: RN EXAM DEVELOPMENT GUIDELINES

COMPETENCIES			
Group A: 50-65% of items	Group B: 20-35% of items	Group C: 5-15% of items	Group D: 1-10% of items

STRUCTURAL VARIABLES

Examination Length and Format	240-260 objective items (e.g., multiple choice)
Test Equating	English and French anchor items are used to accomplish test equating.
Item Presentation	50-60% independent items 40-50% case-based items

Taxonomies for Items
   The Cognitive Domain
 	
   The Affective Domain
	Knowledge/Comprehension: 25-35% of items
	Application: 40-55% of items
	Critical Thinking: 10-20% of items*
	Receiving/Responding
	Valuing } 4-8% of items
	Organization/Characterization
	
	* % of Critical Thinking items are maximized within this range

Competency Categories and Weightings	Data Collection: 9% Analysis and Interpretation of Data: 6% Planning Care: 7% Implementation: 41% Evaluation: 10% Collaboration and Coordination: 4% Professional Practice: 22%

CONTEXTUAL VARIABLES

Client Age and Gender	**Male** **Female** 0 to 18 years 12-18% 12-18% 19 to 64 years 14-20% 15-21% 65+ years 9-15% 20-26%
Client Culture	Items will be included that measure awareness, sensitivity, and respect for different cultural values, beliefs, and practices, without introducing stereotypes.

Client Health Situation	Using the metaparadigm of nursing, and the contextual variables, the elements below are applied in different combinations to develop a cross-section of items.
	
	A. Biophysical
	   Psychosocial
	   Spiritual
	
	B. Common and Predictable Health Situations
	
	C. Health Promotion
	   Illness Prevention
	   Restoration and Maintenance of Health
	   Care of the Dying

Health Care Environment	Since nursing can be practiced in a variety of settings and most of the competencies are not setting dependent, the health care environment is only specified where necessary.

Application occurs when you are required to apply your knowledge in new or practical situations. For example, you would be using application skills when you incorporate principles of nutrition into a health-teaching plan for a person recently diagnosed with diabetes. Approximately half the questions on the RN Exam are at the application level.

Critical Thinking refers to your ability to solve problems. This means formulating valid conclusions and making decisions about nursing care. For example, you have to use your critical thinking skills when prioritizing nursing interventions in a crisis situation. The critical thinking level of the cognitive domain is represented by 10 to 20% of the questions on the RN Exam.

The Affective Domain

The RN Exam is also designed to assess competencies that involve attributes such as attitudes and judgment, that do not fall strictly within the cognitive domain. For the RN Exam, the affective domain is defined to have three levels: (1) Receiving/ Responding; (2) Valuing; and (3) Organization/ Characterization. These levels address such areas as examination of personal values, interpersonal interactions with clients and colleagues, and identification of professional limits. Note that the three levels are not weighted individually; rather, an overall weight of 4 to 8% of the exam is assigned to questions reflecting the affective domain.

COMPETENCY CATEGORIES

For the purpose of the RN Exam, the competencies have been classified within a seven-category classification system, which includes the five steps of the nursing process (Data Collection, Analysis and Interpretation of Data, Planning Care, Implementation, and Evaluation), and two additional categories (Coordination and Collaboration, and Professional Practice).

These categories are defined as follows:

Data Collection

The nurse collects pertinent data based on a conceptual framework of nursing.

Analysis and Interpretation of Data

The nurse analyzes and interprets client data, based on scientific knowledge, a conceptual framework of nursing, the situation, and the client's perception of the situation. The nurse identifies nursing diagnoses.

Planning Care

The nurse, in collaboration with the client (significant persons might be included, depending on the client's wishes), plans nursing care based on the nursing diagnoses.

Implementation

The nurse safely and effectively implements the plan of care and provides nursing interventions.

Evaluation

The nurse, in collaboration with the client, evaluates the effectiveness of the plan of care on an ongoing basis and modifies the plan as necessary.

Collaboration and Coordination

The nurse collaborates with other members of the nursing and health care team to ensure the delivery of safe and comprehensive care.

Professional Practice

The nurse practices within professional, legal, and ethical standards, and monitors practice according to those standards.

CONTEXTUAL VARIABLES

The following four variables set the context for the exam content:

Client Age and Gender

Specifications are provided for the *age* and *gender* of the clients described in the RN Exam. The use of these variables ensures that the clients described in the exam represent the demographic characteristics of the Canadian population encountered by the nurse beginning to practice. Client ages are categorized into three levels: Child and Adolescent (0-18 years); Adult (19-64 years); and Older Adult (65+ years).

Client Culture

Some of the questions on the RN Exam have been included to measure awareness, sensitivity, and respect for different cultures within Canada.

Client Health Situation

Various client health situations are represented on the RN Exam. These health situations are developed from a nursing focus, and reflect different combinations of: (1) client dimensions (i.e., biophysical, psychosocial, spiritual); (2) common and predictable health situations; and (3) nursing roles (i.e., health promotion, illness prevention, restoration and maintenance of health, care of the dying).

Health Care Environment

Questions on the RN Exam are set within particular health care environments only when the specification of a health care environment is required for clarity.

2

HOW THE RN EXAM IS ORGANIZED

The RN Exam is divided into two books, administered over the course of one day; Book 1 is written in the morning, and Book 2 in the afternoon. You will have 3½ hours to write each book. The exam consists of a series of multiple-choice questions, each of which is designed to measure a specific competency expected of nurses beginning to practice.

Each question on the exam, whether in the case or independent format, contains a stem and four options. The stem is typically made up of one to three sentences that provide relevant information or data, and the specific nursing question that is being asked. Of the four options, one is the correct (or best) answer, and the remaining three are incorrect, or less correct options.

Some of the questions in each exam book are *experimental*. That is, they are being tried out to determine their suitability for use on future exams. Although your answers to these experimental questions do not count toward your score, it is important to do your best on each question on the exam because you have no way of knowing which questions are experimental.

The sample case and independent questions on the next page show the type of questions used in the exam. Note that the questions in these examples are not meant to reflect the level of difficulty of the questions on the exam. Correct answers are blackened in the ovals on the right.

SAMPLE QUESTIONS: CASE-BASED

CASE 1

Mr. Robert Lowry, an 82-year-old married man, collapses at home. Mr. Lowry is rushed to the community hospital where it is determined that he has suffered a cerebrovascular accident (CVA). Mrs. Lowry tells the nurse that, prior to this incident, her husband had been taking a thiazide diuretic to control his hypertension.

ITEMS 1 to 5 refer to this case.

1. Which one of the following initial nursing assessments would determine Mr. Lowry's level of consciousness?

    ① ② ③ ●

    1. Visual fields
    2. Auditory acuity
    3. Deep tendon reflexes
    4. Responses to painful stimuli

2. Mr. Lowry regains consciousness and is found to have loss of movement on his left side and hemianopsia. Which one of the following responses by the nurse would be appropriate to give Mrs. Lowry when she asks questions regarding her husband's potential for recovery?

    ① ② ● ④

    1. "It's difficult to know, but most people take at least a year to recover completely."
    2. "It sounds as though you may be somewhat anxious to resume your former lifestyle."
    3. "Concern about recovery is common. Rehabilitation takes time and progress is often slow."
    4. "To be anxious is normal. Unfortunately, there is no way of estimating your husband's recovery potential."

3. Mr. Lowry is receiving a thiazide diuretic. Which one of the following manifestations would indicate mild hypokalemia?

    ● ② ③ ④

    1. Anorexia
    2. Bradycardia
    3. Muscle spasms
    4. Elevated blood pressure

4. Which one of the following interventions should the nurse implement to encourage Mr. Lowry to feed himself?

①②●④

1. Assist him to position the cutlery in his hands.
2. Suggest that Mrs. Lowry take him to the cafeteria.
3. Arrange food items on his tray so he can see them.
4. Allow sufficient time for him to cut up his own food.

5. Which one of the following nursing observations of Mrs. Lowry's behavior would best indicate her readiness to participate in her husband's care at home?

①②③●

1. She visits him every day.
2. She selects his daily menus.
3. She brings his shaving kit and pyjamas from home.
4. She asks if she is correctly positioned to help him walk.

SAMPLE QUESTIONS: INDEPENDENT

1. Which one of the following nursing measures would most likely facilitate a client's acceptance of an altered body image following a total laryngectomy and tracheostomy?

①●③④

1. Demonstrate a sympathetic approach when providing the client's tracheostomy care.
2. Emphasize what the client can do within the limitations resulting from the treatment.
3. Encourage the client's family to refrain from discussing the tracheostomy while visiting.
4. Reassure the client that following discharge there can be a complete return to prehospitalization activities.

2. What should the nurse do if, in the nurse's opinion, the physician's order for a postoperative analgesic seems excessive?

①●③④

1. Assess the client closely for side effects after giving the medication.
2. Seek clarification from the physician before giving the medication.
3. Give the medication and document the concern in the nursing notes.
4. Withhold the medication and document the reason in the nursing notes.

CHAPTER

3

Test-Taking Strategies

TEST-TAKING STRATEGIES

This chapter will help you prepare to write the RN Exam by reviewing what you need to do before and during the exam, what to bring to the examination centre, and how you can best perform on multiple-choice questions.

BEFORE THE RN EXAM

Arrange to Write the RN Exam

If you are interested in writing the RN Exam, you must arrange to do so by contacting the registering/licensing authority in the province in which you wish to write. Their staff will inform you of the documentation you must provide to register for the exam, as well as the fee you will have to pay. A list of RN registering/licensing authorities can be found in Appendix B.

All candidates are entitled to receive a fair and valid assessment. To this end, CNAT, in conjunction with the registering/licensing authorities, will authorize reasonable and appropriate modifications to the RN Exam administration procedures to accommodate candidates with disabilities. For further information, contact your registering/licensing authority.

Read The Canadian RN Exam Prep Guide

This guide contains information that will help you become more familiar with the RN Exam. The rationales for the correct answers (and the incorrect options), and the references listed in the Bibliography, provide an ideal way to review essential nursing content. You are also presented with a variety of ways to use the Prep Guide, depending on how much time you have before you write the RN Exam.

Take the Practice Exam in the Prep Guide

Taking the Practice Exam under conditions that are as close as possible to those of the actual exam is a great way to prepare and to ensure that there will be no surprises. Give yourself the right amount of time to complete each exam book and don't look ahead to the answers. To simulate true exam conditions, arrange to take the Practice Exam with other students who are also interested in preparing for the exam.

Use the Information from your Performance Profile

By conducting an analysis of your performance on the Practice Exam, you will be able to identify your strengths and weaknesses. Use this information to your advantage to focus your studying in areas of weakness. Details on how to create your Performance Profile are found in Chapter 6.

Study Effectively

Select a place that is quiet and free from distractions, yet comfortable for studying. Develop a study plan schedule, dividing your time between specific topics or sections. Keep in mind that five 2-hour sessions are likely to be more beneficial than two 5-hour periods. Monitor your progress and revise your schedule as necessary.

Prepare for the Examination Day

Check the location of the examination centre and examination room, and determine how much time you will need to get there. If necessary, do a practice run and confirm bus schedules or the availability of parking. As well, it is important to be alert and focused when you write the exam—be sure to get plenty of rest, and to eat a suitable breakfast, before you arrive at the examination centre.

WHAT TO BRING TO THE RN EXAM

■ *Identification*

In most cases, you must bring your candidate identification card, issued by your registering/licensing authority. They will also inform you whether you are required to present additional identification.

■ *Pencils / Eraser*

Unless otherwise advised, take two or three medium-soft (HB) pencils and a soft pencil eraser.

■ *A Watch*

Although each examination room will have a clock, and you will be periodically advised of the time, you might prefer to bring your own watch to keep track of the time and gauge your pace.

WHAT NOT TO BRING

Books, paper, notes, calculators and other aids are not permitted in the examination room.

WHAT TO WEAR

Remember that you will be sitting for hours. Wear comfortable clothing.

DURING THE RN EXAM

■ *Listen to All Announcements*

The presiding officer will inform you of important details, such as how long you have to complete the exam, and how and where to hand in your exam book and response sheet, as well as when you should arrive for the second session.

■ *Read the Exam Book Instructions*

Exam instructions are very important. It is essential that you have a clear understanding of what you are expected to do. If you don't understand what you have been told or what you have read, ask questions in the period before the exam officially begins.

■ *Complete All Information Accurately*

You will be required to fill in certain information on your response sheets and exam books (e.g., your candidate number from your identification card). Errors made in completing this information can delay the scoring of your exam. And if you make errors in recording your choice of answer on the exam questions, you will not be given any credit. Be sure that for each question you have recorded a single answer in the appropriate place on the response sheet.

■ *One Question at a Time*

Consider each question as a separate entity. Don't let a difficult question make you anxious as you approach the next one. Do the best you can with each question and move on to the next. Try not to rush, but don't spend more than two or three minutes on any individual question. If you don't know the answer, skip it and return to it later. Something in a subsequent case or question might jog your memory. If you still don't know the answer, don't be afraid to guess. No points are deducted for wrong answers. If you do not answer all the questions in sequence, it is particularly important to ensure that the oval you are filling in on your response sheet is aligned with the correct question number.

When you decide on a correct answer from among the options, immediately indicate your choice on the response sheet before moving on to the next question. Do not circle all the answers in the exam book and transfer them when you are finished the book because you could run out of time, and credit is not given for answers in your exam book—only for answers recorded on your response sheet.

■ *Changing your Answer*

If you decide to change an answer after filling it in on your response sheet, make sure the original choice is completely erased. Otherwise, it will appear as though you have selected two options. This will be scored as a wrong answer. Similarly, avoid making stray marks on your response sheet that the computer could inadvertently pick up as answers to questions.

Be cautious about changing your answer. Very often your first choice is correct. Making a new selection is only advantageous if you are confident that the new option is correct.

Read the Question Carefully

Concentrate on what is being asked in the question and relate it to the data provided. Do not make any assumptions unless they are directly implied.

Pick out important words that relate to the question. For example, in some questions you may be asked for the most appropriate *initial* response by the nurse; but you should be aware that questions that follow may deal with the nurse's most *ethical* response or the nurse's most *therapeutic* response. Reviewing the questions in the Practice Exam will help you to recognize key words that will appear on the RN Exam.

Guessing

There is no penalty for guessing on the RN Exam. You will not lose any marks if you select an incorrect answer.

STRATEGIES FOR MULTIPLE-CHOICE QUESTIONS

Familiarize Yourself with Multiple-Choice Questions

A thorough understanding of multiple-choice questions will allow you to most effectively apply your nursing knowledge and skills to the testing situation.

A multiple-choice question is constructed so that only someone who has mastered the subject matter will select the correct answer; to that person, only one option appears to be the correct answer. To someone who lacks a firm grasp of the subject matter, all options look equally attractive and plausible.

Use a Three-Step Approach

It is often helpful to use the following three-step approach to answer the multiple-choice questions that appear on the RN Exam.

1. Carefully read the information provided in the case text (for cases) and in the stem of the question. Try to understand the client's health situation and the nursing care the client is likely to require.

2. Read the stem carefully. Before looking at the options, make sure you have understood the question. Use the information provided and, based on your nursing knowledge and skills, try to imagine the correct answer.

3. Study the alternatives provided and select the one that comes closest to the answer you imagined. You may wish to reread the stem before finalizing your selection.

Take Advantage of the Process of Elimination

If you are not presented with an option that matches or is close to the one you imagined after reading the stem, try to eliminate some of the options that are absolutely incorrect. The following example illustrates how you can benefit from the process of elimination.

QUESTION

Which one of the following responses by the nurse would best assist Mrs. Montgomery to verbalize her fears when she expresses anxiety about the possibility of having a mastectomy?

1. "I know exactly how you feel about this."
2. "Would you like to talk to the head nurse?"
3. "You seem worried that you may need to have surgery."
4. "It's a normal reaction to be afraid when faced with surgery."

To take full advantage of the process of elimination, it is important to focus on the key idea in the stem. The key idea is assisting the client to verbalize her fears. In Option 1, the spotlight is on the nurse and not on the client or her concerns. Option 1 can be eliminated because it is highly unlikely that any one person knows exactly how someone else feels in a given situation.

Option 2 also fails to address the client's immediate concern because the nurse completely avoids dealing with the client and passes the responsibility on to another team member. For this reason, Option 2 can be eliminated as a possible correct answer.

Option 4 should be eliminated immediately. By telling the client that what she is experiencing is "normal," the nurse implies that the client's situation is routine. Such a response would be depersonalizing and nontherapeutic.

After these three options are systematically eliminated, you can consider Option 3, the correct option, which is open-ended and encourages the client to begin talking about how she feels about her upcoming surgery.

CHECKLIST OF COMMON TEST-TAKING ERRORS

Students often make mistakes on an examination because of errors in processing facts and information, or because of problems with multiple-choice questions. These are technical errors related to writing tests and not related to a lack of nursing knowledge or skills.

As you proceed through the Practice Exam and determine whether you answered questions correctly, you may wish to keep a checklist of problems you had related to your test-taking skills. You can then use the results of this checklist to identify skills that you need to develop during your preparation for the RN Exam.

A Checklist of Common Test-Taking Errors is provided on page 23. Some of the most common errors are listed down the left-hand column. Tick off the particular technical error(s) you made with the questions you answered incorrectly. Keep in mind that you may have more than one technical error with any one question.

CHECKLIST OF COMMON TEST-TAKING ERRORS

Missed important information in the case text	
Misread the stem of the question	
Failed to pick out important or key words in the stem of the question	
Did not relate the question to information in the case text	
Made assumptions in the case text/question	
Focused on insignificant details and missed key issues	
Selected more than one answer	
Incorrectly transferred answer from selection in exam book to computer response sheet	
Switched answer selected	

3

CHAPTER

4

Taking the Practice Exam

TAKING THE PRACTICE EXAM

Like the RN Exam, the Practice Exam consists of two books: Book 1 and Book 2. How you complete the Practice Exam will depend on whether you are using Method A, B, or C (described in Chapter 1). If you are going to take the Practice Exam only once, gain the maximum benefit from this experience by attempting to simulate the actual exam conditions as closely as possible. That means writing the exam in a quiet location, without the benefit of books, notes or other aids, and strictly adhering to the time limit.

Since there are no experimental questions being tested on the Practice Exam (i.e., all the questions will count towards your total score), you should limit yourself to 3 hours per exam book. During the RN Exam, you will have experimental questions in the exam books; therefore, you will be allowed 3½ hours per book.

Read the instructions contained in the Practice Exam carefully, but keep in mind that during your simulation, you will not have the benefit of a presiding officer to remind you of how much time is remaining. The front and back covers of the Practice Exam and the instructions are similar to those on the RN Exam. The instructions indicate that you have 3½ hours (administration time limit for the actual RN Exam) but, as suggested above, you should limit yourself to 3 hours per book during your simulation. On the cover of each Practice Exam book is a *test form number* that is also repeated in the lower left-hand corner of each page of the exam book. This test form number is required by the Canadian Nurses Association for scoring the RN Exam (i.e., not the Practice Exam).

There are blank response sheets included with the *Prep Guide* so that you can gain experience in recording the personal information and filling in the ovals that correspond to your answer selections. Familiarize yourself with the candidate information you will be required to complete when you write the RN Exam.

You should wait until you have finished the entire Practice Exam to calculate your total score and to create your Performance Profile. The information will be complete and, therefore, more accurate and more useful to you. Instructions on calculating your score and determining your Performance Profile are provided in Chapters 5 and 6, which follow the Practice Exam.

4

Canadian Nurses Association

Testing division

Nurse Registration/Licensure Examination

CANDIDATE NUMBER

SIGNATURE

Book 1
Test Form 5109

Read the instructions and sample items inside the front cover

CANADIAN NURSES ASSOCIATION
ASSOCIATION DES INFIRMIÈRES ET INFIRMIERS DU CANADA

INSTRUCTIONS

A) TESTING TIME AND MATERIAL

You will have three and one-half hours to work on this test. The starting and finishing times will be announced and you will be advised when there are 30 and 15 minutes working time remaining. If at any time you have any questions about what you should do, raise your hand and an invigilator will assist you.

You will be advised whether you may leave the examination room if you finish the test before the time is up. You must *stop* working when the signal is given. An invigilator will check your test book and answer sheet *before* you leave.

Clear your desk of all materials except your identification card, response sheet, test book, pencils, and eraser. Do *not* fold, bend, or tear your answer sheet, as this could affect the scoring of your test.

B) ANSWER SHEET

Use the diagram on the back cover of your test book as a guide for filling in the boxes in the identification portion of your answer sheet. Enter in your CANDIDATE NUMBER, the WRITING CENTRE CODE, and the TEST FORM and fill in the corresponding ovals. If you do not have a candidate number leave this section blank. Complete the box labeled LANGUAGE OF WRITING.

Be sure the mark you make for each answer is black, fills the oval, and contains the number corresponding to the number of the answer you have chosen. Do *not* fill in more than one oval for an item or you will get no credit for it. Erase *completely* any answer you wish to change and mark your new choice in the correct oval. An incomplete erasure may be read incorrectly as an intended answer. Do not press too heavily on your pencil or you may damage the answer sheet.

Note that the items on the answer sheet are numbered in columns. There are fewer items in the test book than there are numbers on the answer sheet.

Make no stray marks on the response sheet; they may count against you. You may use the margins of the test book for any scratch work, but you will *not* get credit for anything you write in the test book.

C) TEST BOOKLET

Sign your name on the line on the cover of this booklet and copy your candidate number into the appropriate boxes. If you do not have a candidate number, *print* your name under your signature.

Read each item carefully and choose the answer you think is *correct*. If you cannot decide on an answer to an item, go on to the next one and come back to this item later if you have time. Try to answer all items. Marks are not subtracted for wrong answers. If you are not sure of an answer, it will be to your advantage to guess. It will probably be best to start at the beginning of the test and work through the items in order.

This examination contains a number of experimental items being tested for future use. Your answers to these items will *not* count toward your score. Because you will not be able to tell which items are experimental, you should do your best on all items, but do *not* spend too much time on any item.

The items in the examination may be presented in nursing cases or as independant items. The context of some cases may seem similar to others in your test book. This reflects current practice where a nurse may have to care for different clients with similar problems. Each case, however, tests different nursing content. The sample case on the next page shows the types of items used. Correct answers are blackened in the ovals on the right.

SAMPLE CASE

Mr. Robert Lowry, an 82-year-old married man, collapses at home. Mr. Lowry is rushed to the community hospital where it is determined that he has suffered a cerebrovascular accident (CVA). Mrs. Lowry tells the nurse that, prior to this incident, her husband had been taking a thiazide diuretic to control his hypertension.

ITEMS 1 to 5 refer to this case.

1. Which of the following initial nursing assessments would determine Mr. Lowry's level of consciousness?

    1. Visual fields
    2. Auditory acuity
    3. Deep tendon reflexes
    4. Responses to painful stimuli

2. Mr. Lowry regains consciousness and is found to have loss of movement on his left side and hemi-anopsia. Which one of the following responses by the nurse would be appropriate to give Mrs. Lowry when she asks questions regarding her husband's potential for recovery?

    1. "It's difficult to know, but most people take at least a year to recover completely."
    2. "It sounds as though you may be somewhat anxious to resume your former lifestyle."
    3. "Concern about recovery is common. Rehabilitation takes time and progress is often slow."
    4. "To be anxious is normal. Unfortunately, there is no way of estimating your husband's recovery potential."

3. Mr. Lowry is receiving a thiazide diuretic. Which one of the following manifestations would indicate mild hypokalemia?

    1. Anorexia
    2. Bradycardia
    3. Muscle spasms
    4. Elevated blood pressure

4. Which of the following interventions should the nurse implement to encourage Mr. Lowry to feed himself?

    1. Assist him to position the cutlery in his hands.
    2. Suggest that Mrs. Lowry take him to the cafeteria.
    3. Arrange food items on his tray so he can see them.
    4. Allow sufficient time for him to cut up his own food.

①②●④

5. Which one of the following nursing observations of Mrs. Lowry's behavior would best indicate her readiness to participate in her husband's care at home?

    1. She visits him every day.
    2. She selects his daily menus.
    3. She brings his shaving kit and pyjamas from home.
    4. She asks if she is correctly positioned to help him walk.

①②③●

END OF SAMPLE CASE

DO NOT OPEN YOUR TEST BOOK OR BEGIN WORKING
UNTIL THE SIGNAL IS GIVEN TO DO SO

CASE 1

Mrs. Kowalski, 69 years old, has recently been admitted to a nursing home because a progression of the osteoarthritis in her hands and hips has made mobilization and self-care difficult. Her primary language is Polish, but she understands English.

ITEMS 1 to 6 refer to this case.

1. Mrs. Kowalski is 155 cm tall and weighs 72 kg. A goal for Mrs. Kowalski is to reduce weight by increasing her knowledge regarding meal planning. How would the nurse best assist Mrs. Kowalski in achieving this goal?
    1. Offer her printed information on weight reduction.
    2. Meet with her and the dietitian to discuss her food preferences.
    3. Suggest that her family bring in her favorite foods which are high in calcium and vitamin D.
    4. Explain to her that her extra weight is causing her joints to become overburdened, resulting in increased pain.

2. Mrs. Kowalski has been complaining of stomach upset after her morning dose of indomethacin (Indocin/Indocid) 80 mg, p.o., b.i.d. The medication is administered at 10 00 hours and 22 00 hours. Which one of the following interventions would ensure safe administration of this medication?
    1. Administer the indomethacin per rectum.
    2. Administer the indomethacin with a laxative.
    3. Change the administration time to correspond with meals.
    4. Request that the total daily maximum dose of indomethacin be reduced.

3. Mrs. Kowalski has been experiencing a flare-up of her osteoarthritis. The physiotherapist has recommended that she follow a regimen of daily exercise. Which one of the following exercise plans would best promote circulation for Mrs. Kowalski?
    1. Isometric exercises
    2. Passive range-of-motion exercises
    3. Performing all activities of daily living
    4. Low-impact endurance exercises such as walking

4. Which one of the following activity plans would best suit Mrs. Kowalski on a day when joint inflammation is mild?

    1. Rest after breakfast; group activity therapy; then a tub bath.
    2. Breakfast at 08 00 hours; warm soaks to arms and hands for 15 minutes; then bed rest for 1 hour.
    3. Isometric and isotonic exercises; ice bag applications to hips and knees; then analgesic administration.
    4. Paraffin wax baths to knees and ankles at 11 00 hours; active range-of-motion exercise; then lunch at 12 00 hours.

5. When Mrs. Kowalski goes to sleep at night, the nurse must ensure that proper body alignment is maintained. Which one of the following nursing actions would be most appropriate?

    1. Apply a wrist splint.
    2. Administer a bedtime analgesic.
    3. Suggest that Mrs. Kowalski wear lightweight but warm bedclothes.
    4. Place a pillow under her superior knee while she is lying in a lateral position.

6. Mrs. Kowalski's nurse used to work on a surgical unit. The nurse has requested further education in long-term gerontological care. Which one of the following in-service sessions would be most appropriate for the nurse to attend?

    1. Dance therapy for the elderly
    2. Rehabilitation care techniques
    3. Management of auxiliary personnel
    4. Community resources available upon discharge

END OF CASE 1

CASE 2

Jane White, 24 years old, has had an uneventful first pregnancy. Jane arrives at the birthing centre accompanied by her partner. Nursing assessment data include:
- gestation: 40 weeks;
- vital signs: BP: 120/78 mmHg; P: 82 beats/min; T: 37° C by mouth;
- contractions: 3-5 minutes apart, 40-50 seconds duration.

ITEMS 7 to 11 refer to this case.

GO TO NEXT PAGE

7. Jane is moaning and requests medication for pain. How should the nurse select the site for administration of an analgesic into the ventrogluteal muscle?

    1. Palpate the lower edge of the acromion process.
    2. Divide the area between the greater trochanter of the femur and the lateral femoral condyle into thirds.
    3. Place the heel of the hand over the greater trochanter of the femur, and form a V between the index and third finger.
    4. Palpate the posterosuperior iliac spine and the greater trochanter, and draw an imaginary line between these landmarks.

8. The nurse assists Jane into the supine position. Jane's blood pressure is now 90/60 mmHg. Which nursing intervention is indicated in response to this change in Jane's condition?

    1. Raise the head of the bed 45°, recheck blood pressure.
    2. Position Jane in the left lateral position, recheck blood pressure.
    3. Maintain Jane in a supine position, monitor blood pressure every 15 minutes.
    4. Place Jane in the knee-chest position, monitor blood pressure every 30 minutes.

9. Which one of the following actions would indicate that the nurse understands the guidelines for universal precautions?

    1. Gowns are worn when handling linen.
    2. Needles are recapped following injection.
    3. Gloves are worn during changing of perineal pads.
    4. Masks are worn by the support partner during delivery.

10. Nursing assessment during the initial postpartum period indicates that Jane is cold and clammy, and has a pulse rate of 120 beats/minute with rapid, shallow respirations. Upon analysis of this data, which of the following actions should the nurse take?

    1. Place Jane in the shock position, notify the physician.
    2. Notify the nursing supervisor, instruct Jane to remain in bed.
    3. Place Jane in Fowler's position, cover her with a warm blanket.
    4. Massage the fundus in a circular motion, note the amount of blood loss.

11. Jane states that Nurse Smith provided excellent assistance when she experienced difficulty with breastfeeding. What action by Nurse Andrews would demonstrate respect for the colleague, Nurse Smith?

    1. Ask Jane to discuss her comments with the nursing supervisor.
    2. Tell Nurse Smith how much Jane appreciated the care provided.
    3. Ask Jane to include her comments on the hospital evaluation form.
    4. Report the comments to the nursing supervisor to record on Nurse Smith's performance appraisal.

END OF CASE 2

CASE 3

Roberta is a 2-year-old girl who is admitted to the pediatric unit of the local hospital. Her parents report that she was well until 2 days ago when she developed flu-like symptoms, fever, anorexia, and lethargy. A diagnosis of bacterial meningitis is confirmed.

ITEMS 12 to 17 refer to this case.

12. Which one of the following pieces of information is significant for the nurse to note concerning Roberta's diagnosis of bacterial meningitis?
    1. She is an only child.
    2. She plays outdoors daily.
    3. She attends a community daycare.
    4. She sleeps in her parents' bedroom.

13. Which one of the following entries in Roberta's chart would best document the nurse's assessment?
    1. Decreased activity, vomiting
    2. Unable to move head, irritable
    3. High fever, complains of headache
    4. Cries with position changes, face flushed

14. Which one of the following actions by the nurse would prevent transmission of the infection?
    1. Follow hospital policy for reporting communicable diseases.
    2. Immediately implement strict isolation precautions for a minimum of 7 days.
    3. Inform Roberta's parents of the probable complications that occur with bacterial meningitis.
    4. Instruct Roberta's mother that all utensils and bedding used by Roberta in the past 2 days need to be sterilized.

15. The nurse is evaluating the care of Roberta's I.V. Which one of the following observations indicates that corrective action is required?
    1. The I.V. is being assessed every hour.
    2. The I.V. is running through an infusion pump.
    3. The I.V. site is covered by a transparent dressing.
    4. The I.V. arm board is removed when her mother visits.

GO TO NEXT PAGE

16. How should the nurse promote a balance between sleep, rest, and activity in caring for Roberta?

    1. Encourage participation in playroom activities.
    2. Advise her parents to visit frequently for short periods of time.
    3. Organize nursing care to provide for extended periods without disturbances.
    4. Provide a bright and cheerful atmosphere during the day and subdued lighting at night.

17. In planning for Roberta's discharge, which one of the following actions should the nurse take?

    1. Instruct the parents to keep Roberta home from daycare.
    2. Ensure an appointment for audiometric testing has been scheduled.
    3. Advise her parents to make an appointment for Roberta with the family dentist.
    4. Complete a referral to the hospital dietitian for assessment of Roberta's nutritional needs.

END OF CASE 3

CASE 4

Mrs. Bells is a 64-year-old widow who recently moved into an apartment. She is admitted to the medical unit for treatment of an acute asthma attack.

ITEMS 18 to 23 refer to this case.

18. In which one of the following positions should the nurse place Mrs. Bells when she is first admitted to the unit?

    1. Supine
    2. Recovery
    3. High-Fowler's
    4. Left lateral with pillow support

19. Which one of the following environmental factors is most likely to have precipitated Mrs. Bells' asthma attack?

    1. Fresh paint in her new apartment
    2. Exposure to an increased number of people
    3. Taking her pet bird to her new apartment
    4. Proximity of her new apartment to the botanical garden

20. Which one of the following pieces of information regarding Mrs. Bells' condition would be most important to include in the end-of-shift report?
    1. Decreased appetite
    2. Increased restlessness
    3. Increased urinary output
    4. Generalized expiratory wheezing

21. Which one of the following statements by the nurse is most appropriate when teaching Mrs. Bells the correct procedure for using her hand-held inhaler?
    1. "Wait at least 30 seconds between puffs."
    2. "Inhale deeply before taking the first puff."
    3. "Hold the mouthpiece 15 cm from your mouth."
    4. "Do not shake the canister before administration."

22. The nurse gives Mrs. Bells her metered dose inhaler of beclomethasone (Beclovent). Which one of the following statements by Mrs. Bells would indicate that additional teaching is required?
    1. "I keep my inhalers with me at all times."
    2. "I use my bronchodilator inhaler before my Beclovent."
    3. "I drink water because the medication bothers my throat."
    4. "I used this medication during my attack but it didn't help."

23. Mrs. Bells says, "I guess the rest of my life will require a lot of time spent in hospitals." Which one of the following responses by the nurse is honest and sincere?
    1. "Most people eventually learn to manage their asthmatic attacks themselves."
    2. "You're lucky your new apartment is so close to the hospital and you can get here quickly."
    3. "You may need to be admitted from time to time, but we can teach you ways to manage your condition."
    4. "Your physician will help you organize your medications so that you are not likely to have further admissions."

END OF CASE 4

CASE 5

Mr. Robinson, age 57, is admitted to hospital with a suspected bowel obstruction. Following diagnostic tests, he is prepared for a bowel resection.

ITEMS 24 to 29 refer to this case.

24. Which one of the following statements by the nurse would best explain to Mr. Robinson the purpose of undergoing a barium enema?
    1. "The x-ray will show if there is a problem in your small intestine."
    2. "The barium may stimulate your bowel and open up the obstruction."
    3. "The test will help the doctor to determine if there is a blockage in your bowel."
    4. "It is important to completely empty the bowel before the doctor operates on it."

25. The nurse plans to conduct preoperative teaching with Mr. Robinson. Which one of the following nursing actions would be most appropriate prior to teaching?
    1. Evaluate his level of reading skills.
    2. Help him to identify what he needs to know.
    3. Review the preoperative teaching checklist with him.
    4. Arrange for his wife to be present for the teaching session.

26. Following surgery, Mr. Robinson complains of severe abdominal pain. Meperidine hydrochloride (Demerol) 100 mg I.M., q. 4h, ordered by the physician, was administered 2 hours ago. Which one of the following nursing actions would be appropriate?
    1. Administer another dose of the medication if vital signs are stable.
    2. Divide the dose in half, giving 50 mg now and the remaining 50 mg in 2 hours.
    3. Explain to Mr. Robinson that it is too early to receive any more medication for pain.
    4. Notify the physician that Mr. Robinson's pain is not being relieved with the present order.

27. Which one of the following nursing actions would maintain universal precautions?
    1. Place soiled linen in an isolation bag.
    2. Check Mr. Robinson's chart for HIV and hepatitis test results.
    3. Wear gloves to empty Mr. Robinson's nasogastric suction bottle.
    4. Use sterile technique to change Mr. Robinson's abdominal dressing.

28.   As the nurse prepares to ambulate Mr. Robinson for the first time postoperatively, his bed becomes fixed in the raised position with the head of the bed flat. Which one of the following nursing actions would best promote Mr. Robinson's safety?

1.   Transfer him to a functioning bed.
2.   Help him out of bed with the assistance of a colleague.
3.   Utilize a footstool when assisting him to step to the floor.
4.   Prop him with pillows while keeping the side rails in place.

29.   Which one of the following actions should the nurse take to help reduce Mr. Robinson's incisional pain?

1.   Assess his anxiety level.
2.   Allow him to rest for an hour before getting up.
3.   Position him on his side, with knees flexed, and a pillow between his legs.
4.   Reassure him that some pain is to be expected and that it will get better every day.

END OF CASE 5

CASE 6

Julie Rogers, age 55, comes to the community health clinic complaining of headaches and ankle edema. The nurse notes that Mrs. Rogers is overweight. On arrival, her BP is 150/110 mmHg. She is diagnosed with essential hypertension and is started on chlorothiazide (Diuril) 500 mg p.o. b.i.d.

ITEMS 30 to 34 refer to this case.

30.   Which one of the following assessments, recorded by the nurse, would have the greatest influence on Mrs. Rogers' condition?

1.   Drinks one cup of coffee per day
2.   Drinks alcohol on special occasions
3.   Smokes one package of cigarettes a day
4.   Father died at age 65 with prostatic cancer

GO TO NEXT PAGE

31. The nurse discovers that Mrs. Rogers prepares all her meals with lard and especially enjoys her foods when flavored with salt. Which one of the following nursing diagnoses best describes this situation?

    1. Noncompliance related to hypertension
    2. Ineffective coping related to hypertension
    3. Alteration in nutrition related to dietary habits
    4. Alteration in elimination related to fluid volume deficit

32. Which one of the following findings would indicate to the nurse that Mrs. Rogers is responding positively to her chlorothiazide (Diuril)?

    1. A potassium level of 6 mEq/L
    2. Blood pressure of 150/110 mmHg
    3. An increase of 1 kg/day in her weight
    4. Negative fluid balance of 500 mL per day

33. Nurse Green reports that Mrs. Rogers is still unsure of what foods are low in sodium, even though Nurse Smith completed the teaching yesterday. Nurse Green suggests that giving Mrs. Rogers some sample menus would help. Which one of the following responses by Nurse Smith demonstrates an openness to new ideas?

    1. "It sounds as if you think I am not qualified to care for Mrs. Rogers."
    2. "In the past, I have found that giving sample menus confuses clients."
    3. "Mrs. Rogers expressed concern over meals; maybe some sample menus will help."
    4. "I think that providing sample menus is more appropriately performed by a dietitian."

34. Before giving Mrs. Rogers her antihypertensive medication, Nurse Jones neglects to check Mrs. Roger's blood pressure. Nurse Black, realizing this omission, tells Nurse Jones, "You should always check the blood pressure before administering the antihypertensive." Which one of the following responses would be most appropriate for Nurse Jones to make?

    1. "It's only a blood pressure; I don't think any harm was done."
    2. "I already knew that; it was included in my orientation material."
    3. "I must remember that; does that apply to all antihypertensive medications?"
    4. "I didn't think the blood pressure had to be checked if it was within the normal range."

END OF CASE 6

CASE 7

Tyler Jones is a 4-year-old boy who was diagnosed with cystic fibrosis during infancy. Since Tyler has experienced frequent respiratory infections in the past, the home care nurse visits regularly to monitor his situation and provide teaching to the family.

ITEMS 35 to 41 refer to this case.

35. Because Tyler dislikes his treatment sessions, his mother performs postural drainage and percussion only when he is in the prone position watching television. The nurse should emphasize that postural drainage and percussion will be optimized when Tyler is in which of the following positions?
    1. Sitting upright to drain the superior segments
    2. In a supine position to drain the posterior segments
    3. In a variety of positions to allow for drainage of all segments
    4. Positioned with his chest lower than his abdomen to drain the anterior segments

36. Mrs. Jones indicates that both she and her husband are frustrated with Tyler's lack of cooperation during his postural drainage and percussion sessions. She also comments that they need help with this aspect of Tyler's care. Which one of the following nursing interventions is most appropriate to facilitate their learning?
    1. Discuss the proper techniques for performing postural drainage and percussion.
    2. Suggest that the respiratory therapist visit daily to perform the postural drainage and percussion.
    3. Recommend that the treatments be done less often until the child is older and more cooperative.
    4. Assess the parents' understanding of growth and development when formulating a teaching plan to address their needs.

37. Mrs. Jones is worried that Tyler's illness has had a detrimental effect on his development, particularly his speech. Which one of the following assessment tools would be most appropriate for the nurse to use to evaluate Tyler's language development?
    1. Apgar score
    2. Snellen Screening Test
    3. Intelligence Quotient (IQ) Test
    4. Denver Developmental Screening Test

38. How should the nurse evaluate the effectiveness of health teaching with Tyler?

    1. Watch him prepare his medications.
    2. Tell him to describe to his mother what cystic fibrosis is.
    3. Ask him if he understands everything that has been taught.
    4. Ask him to point out different areas for chest physiotherapy on a doll.

39. Which one of the following practices by Tyler's mother would suggest a need for additional teaching by the home care nurse?

    1. Decreasing pancreatic enzymes if Tyler is constipated.
    2. Increasing pancreatic enzymes as Tyler's food intake increases.
    3. Administering pancreatic enzymes in the morning and at bedtime.
    4. Increasing pancreatic enzymes if Tyler's stools are large and bulky.

40. Mrs. Jones appears to be coping well, but she states that there are times when she feels very alone when dealing with the chronic aspects of Tyler's condition. Which one of the following responses by the nurse would be most appropriate?

    1. "You seem depressed; talking to a counselor may relieve some of your concerns."
    2. "You appear to be coping fairly well. Although things may seem difficult now, they will improve."
    3. "I'm surprised you still feel this way. Most people who have children with cystic fibrosis find it less stressful by the end of the first year."
    4. "Many families who have children with cystic fibrosis experience similar feelings. Would you like me to arrange for you to talk with one of those families?"

41. The home care agency requests that the nurse caring for Tyler perform a new intravenous procedure on him, but they do not provide the nurse with the policy that accompanies the procedure. What should the nurse do?

    1. Check the intravenous policies at the local hospital.
    2. Discuss the situation with the immediate nursing supervisor.
    3. Carry out the procedure but document that no policy existed.
    4. Contact the nursing practice consultant of the provincial/territorial nurses association.

END OF CASE 7

CASE 8

Jackie, age 23, arrives at the emergency department of a small community hospital immediately after being sexually assaulted. The nurse is part of the multidisciplinary team that provides immediate care for Jackie.

ITEMS 42 to 47 refer to this case.

42. Which one of the following principles is most important for the nurse to follow when providing immediate nursing care for Jackie?
    1. Physical touch may be interpreted as a violation.
    2. Waiting rooms with numerous people enhance feelings of safety.
    3. Decision-making places undue strain on the victim and should be managed by the nurse.
    4. Legal terminology is less threatening and minimizes the victim's tendency to relive the experience.

43. Jackie is reluctant to talk about the assault during the initial history. Which one of the following statements by the nurse would best facilitate communication with her?
    1. "I can see this is very hard for you. Go slowly and start at the beginning if you can."
    2. "It's difficult to talk about this but I can't help you unless you tell me what happened."
    3. "Instead of talking, just nod to respond to my questions. Were you forced to have sex with your assailant?"
    4. "Try not to think about it, we'll take care of everything. It's best if you talk about something else right now."

44. Jackie asks the nurse why she must undergo so many tests before being allowed to bathe. What information is most important for the nurse to consider before responding to Jackie's question?
    1. Jackie can wash as long as she does not immerse herself in a bath.
    2. The police must conduct their investigation prior to Jackie bathing.
    3. Specific procedures regarding bathing must be followed to ensure legal evidence is not destroyed.
    4. Jackie must have prophylactic treatment for pregnancy and sexually transmitted diseases before bathing is allowed.

GO TO NEXT PAGE

45. Which one of the following nursing actions is most important when the nurse prepares Jackie for an internal pelvic examination?
    1. Closely inspect Jackie for perineal lacerations and bruising.
    2. Show Jackie the equipment that will be used in the examination.
    3. Explain to Jackie the procedures that will be included in the examination.
    4. Place Jackie on the examination table and position her legs in the stirrups.

46. The nurse is questioned by another nurse about the circumstances that led to Jackie's assault. Which one of the following responses by the nurse is most in keeping with the role of an advocate for client confidentiality?
    1. "That information isn't relevant to Jackie's care."
    2. "She's a victim and what happened was criminal."
    3. "Read her story in the chart for the circumstances."
    4. "It's hard to say what really happened; she didn't give a clear history."

47. Which one of the following actions falls within the nurse's scope of practice?
    1. Offer to provide ongoing support to Jackie if she decides to initiate legal proceedings.
    2. Propose to drive Jackie home at the end of the nurse's work shift to ensure Jackie's safety.
    3. Initiate mandatory contact with the police department to report that a sexual assault has occurred.
    4. Draw ordered blood samples from Jackie to decrease the number of hospital personnel with whom Jackie must interact.

END OF CASE 8

INDEPENDENT ITEMS

ITEMS 48 to 100 do not refer to a case.

48. When preparing medication for administration to a child, which one of the following factors is most appropriate for the nurse to apply in calculating a safe dosage?
    1. Child's age
    2. Child's metabolic rate
    3. Child's body surface area
    4. Percentage of the adult dosage

45

49. Postoperatively, Mrs. Romanescu's hemoglobin is low and she is to receive a blood transfusion. Which one of the following nursing interventions is most appropriate to perform when administering blood?

    1. Monitor hemoglobin and tissue turgor.
    2. Monitor vital signs and ensure an I.V. of normal saline solution.
    3. Monitor urine output and ensure an I.V. of 5% dextrose solution.
    4. Monitor urine output and assess for a hemolytic reaction every 30 minutes.

50. Mr. Thomas is a client with ascites. How should the nurse position Mr. Thomas to promote comfort?

    1. Sims'
    2. Prone
    3. High-Fowler's
    4. Semi-Fowler's

51. Angela is a 24-year-old woman who has given birth to her second child. Which one of the following initial assessments should the nurse make to determine Angela's learning needs for providing baby care?

    1. Observe Angela as she feeds her baby.
    2. Have Angela perform a baby bath demonstration.
    3. Ask Angela if she knows anything about baby care.
    4. Inquire about Angela's previous experience with babies.

52. Which one of the following ordered p.r.n. medications would be appropriate for the nurse to administer to relieve pain in a client with a myocardial infarction?

    1. Lorazepam (Ativan)
    2. Acetominophen (Tylenol)
    3. Morphine sulfate (Morphine)
    4. Magnesium hydroxide (Maalox)

53. Mrs. Smith is scheduled for removal of abdominal sutures. The nurse observes that the incision line is red, swollen, and draining at the distal end. Which of the following actions best demonstrate the application of sound judgment by the nurse?

    1. Cleaning the incision, removing alternate sutures, and applying a sterile dressing.
    2. Taking a culture of the drainage, cleaning the incision, and recording the information in the nurses' notes.
    3. Taking a culture of the drainage, cleaning the incision, applying a sterile dressing, and notifying the physician.
    4. Cleaning the incision, applying a hot compress, covering with a sterile dressing, and notifying the nursing supervisor.

54. While positioning a 4-year-old unconscious client on his side, the nurse decides to perform oral and nasal suctioning. Which one of the following nursing actions would be most appropriate for this procedure?

1. Place him in a semi-Fowler's position.
2. Set the wall suction unit at 110 to 120 mmHg.
3. Lubricate the catheter tip with a water-soluble lubricant.
4. Apply suction while slowly rotating and withdrawing the catheter.

55. Ms. Drake is a 70-year-old woman who consulted the nurse for treatment of urinary dribbling. On a return visit 2 months later, which one of the following questions should the nurse ask to determine how Ms. Drake views her progress to date?

1. "Are you more confident about going out?"
2. "Do you feel you have to practice your exercises as often now?"
3. "Are there fewer situations where you have problems with dribbling?"
4. "Do you feel you are somewhat successful in controlling your incontinence?"

56. Which one of the following facts about a nursing colleague should the nurse report to the appropriate authority?

1. History of drug dependency
2. Inconsistency in following dress code
3. Failure to purchase liability insurance
4. Failure to follow the standards of practice

57. Natalie is a 4-year-old girl suffering from pediculosis and impetigo. Which one of the following statements would be most appropriate for the community health nurse to use with Natalie's family when teaching them about infection control?

1. "Natalie must be isolated to prevent the spread of infection."
2. "It is important not to be overprotective of Natalie. This could stifle her emotional growth."
3. "You must prevent further excoriation of Natalie's skin, to keep secondary infections from occurring."
4. "Natalie's skin needs to be kept clean and dry. She needs to wear clean clothes daily and have her sheets and pillow case changed."

58. The nurse admits Rachel Sales, a 29-year-old childless woman who has severe pain due to pelvic inflammatory disease. Following introductions, which one of the following comments by the nurse would be most appropriate to open the interview?

1. "What is your understanding of your present condition?"
2. "It must be frightening for you to be experiencing such severe pain."
3. "Do you know of any substances to which you've had an allergic reaction?"
4. "The possibility of losing your childbearing ability must be difficult for you."

59. Marcia, a 12-year-old girl, is scheduled for a colonoscopy and is unaware that she is undergoing the procedure. Which one of the following actions would demonstrate that the nurse is acting as a client advocate?

    1. Explaining to Marcia the procedure for the colonoscopy.
    2. Notifying the physician that Marcia needs an explanation of the procedure.
    3. Calling Marcia's family to have them explain to her what they have been told.
    4. Requesting that a nurse from the gastrointestinal clinic discuss the procedure with Marcia.

60. A nurse on a surgical ward is caring for a 48-year-old man who had a cholecystectomy 4 days ago. The surgeon is satisfied with the client's progress and recommends that the nurse remove the T-tube. Which one of the following interventions by the nurse is most appropriate?

    1. Remove the T-tube using sterile technique and a dressing tray.
    2. Advise the surgeon that the T-tube should be removed by a physician.
    3. Discuss with other nursing colleagues how this task should be completed.
    4. Call in the nursing supervisor, who is more qualified and experienced in T-tube removal.

61. In cardiopulmonary resuscitation, which one of the following actions should the nurse take first?

    1. Assess the carotid pulse.
    2. Verify that the client is unresponsive.
    3. Place the client on a hard, firm surface.
    4. Implement the head-tilt, chin-lift manoeuvre.

62. Mr. Patrick O'Reilly is a 35-year-old who has recently been diagnosed with insulin-dependent (Type I) diabetes. Mr. O'Reilly appears overwhelmed and expresses concern about being able to manage the prescribed regimen involved in controlling his diabetes. What would be the best approach by the nurse to facilitate the client's management of his diabetes?

    1. Have Mr. O'Reilly's friend attend teaching sessions about insulin administration.
    2. Explain blood glucose monitoring to Mr. O'Reilly, and have him perform a return demonstration.
    3. Encourage Mr. O'Reilly to verbalize his fears and introduce him to another diabetic client who is of a similar age.
    4. Give Mr. O'Reilly pamphlets on the manifestations of hyperglycemia and hypoglycemia so that he may read them at home.

63. Sixty-four-year-old Ms. MacDonald is 2 days postoperative following an abdominal hysterectomy. The nurse caring for Ms. MacDonald is assisting her with a morning bath and observes that the abdominal dressing is saturated with fresh blood. What actions should the nurse take?

    1. Stop the bed bath and take Ms. MacDonald's blood pressure.
    2. Firmly press a clean towel over the saturated dressing and call for assistance.
    3. Remove the saturated dressing and place two new sterile dressings over the incision.
    4. Go to the supply cart for a sterile abdominal dressing and reinforce the original dressing.

64. Which one of the following pieces of assessment data would be most useful to the nurse in identifying early evidence of hypokalemia?

    1. Enhanced alertness and anxiety
    2. Prolonged use of a thiazide diuretic
    3. Hyperactive bowel sounds and diarrhea
    4. History of chronic dietary potassium deficiency

65. Which one of the following nursing interventions should the nurse perform initially to promote comfort for a client experiencing acute pain related to renal calculi?

    1. Encourage frequent voiding.
    2. Apply moist heat to the flank area.
    3. Administer analgesics as prescribed.
    4. Provide distraction by ambulating.

66. The physician has prescribed cromolyn sodium (Intal) for Aaron, age 6, who has poorly controlled asthma. When providing teaching for Aaron's parents, the nurse should explain that the cromolyn sodium (Intal) is used for which of the following reasons?

    1. To prevent asthma attacks.
    2. To relieve allergic symptoms.
    3. To reduce inflammation in the airways.
    4. To relax the smooth muscles of the bronchi.

67. The nurse observes a nursing colleague falsifying the client's medication record. After speaking with the colleague, who is the appropriate authority to contact about this incident?

    1. The pharmacist
    2. The nurses' union
    3. The nursing supervisor
    4. The nurses' professional association

68. The goal for the client is to heal a decubitus ulcer. Which one of the following statements best reflects the expected outcome for this goal?
    1. The client will be repositioned q. 2h.
    2. The client's ulcer will show evidence of the healing process.
    3. The client's ulcer will decrease in size by 1 cm within 1 week.
    4. The client will be positioned to avoid pressure on the ulcerated area.

69. An experienced nurse has recently been appointed to a leadership role within a unit in the health care facility. Which of the following behaviors by the nurse best demonstrates effective leadership skills?
    1. Directing activities of others during a crisis situation.
    2. Limiting discussion following the end-of-shift report to 5 minutes.
    3. Determining facility policies and directing their implementation on the unit.
    4. Making client assignments according to individual staff members' preferences.

70. Mrs. Dorchester, age 89, is admitted after a fall down a flight of stairs. Which of the following data should the nurse collect first upon admitting the client to the unit?
    1. Stability of gait
    2. Acuity of vision
    3. Level of consciousness
    4. Condition of extremities

71. Curtis, 4 months old, is hospitalized because of a weak cough, wheezy respirations, and irritability. Which one of the following nursing diagnoses should the nurse establish as a priority?
    1. Altered nutrition related to coughing episodes
    2. Sleep pattern disturbance related to hospitalization
    3. Impaired gas exchange related to pulmonary congestion
    4. Ineffective airway clearance related to constricted airways

72. Mrs. Yee, age 79, is receiving intravenous therapy through a central venous line. Which one of the following interventions should be part of the routine care for Mrs. Yee and her central line?
    1. Report any dyspnea or chest pain.
    2. Check her line for blood return daily.
    3. Constantly monitor her insertion site visually.
    4. Flush her line with 30 mL of normal saline each shift.

GO TO NEXT PAGE

73. Ms. Jacobs, age 37, returns to the unit following a bunionectomy. After determining that the client is experiencing considerable incisional pain, which one of the following actions should the nurse take?

    1. Wait until Ms. Jacobs requests an analgesic.
    2. Return later to further assess Ms. Jacobs' level of pain.
    3. Administer an oral, non-narcotic analgesic as the first means of pain control.
    4. Prepare and administer a narcotic analgesic according to the physician's order.

74. While reviewing clients' charts, the nurse notes that Jim is on AZT (Retrovir). The nurse's best friend, Mary, is soon to be married to Jim, and is unaware of his illness. Which one of the following actions best indicates that the nurse is practicing within the code of ethics?

    1. The nurse flags Jim's chart to indicate that he is HIV positive.
    2. The nurse informs Mary that she is at risk for contracting HIV.
    3. The nurse asks to be assigned to another case because of her friendship with Mary.
    4. The nurse asks Jim if he intends to tell Mary about his illness before the wedding.

75. Janet Kiley has just delivered a 36-week stillborn baby. Which of the following nursing actions would be most appropriate at this time?

    1. Ask a volunteer from the self-help grieving group to visit Janet.
    2. Ensure that no one enters Janet's room and interrupts her grieving.
    3. Remind the physician to obtain Janet's permission for an autopsy of the baby.
    4. Identify Janet's needs with her and involve the social worker when planning her care.

76. The nurse caring for a 65-year-old female client with left ventricular failure observes that the client has an anxious expression, is cyanosed, and is severely dyspneic. The nurse checks the client's vital signs and notes that respirations are slow, pulse is very rapid, and she is expectorating large amounts of pink frothy sputum. Which one of the following nursing actions demonstrates the nurse's accurate interpretation of data?

    1. Suction the secretions and request an order for chest physiotherapy.
    2. Notify the physician that the client is showing complications of left ventricular failure.
    3. Place the client in a semi-prone position to facilitate drainage of secretions from the respiratory tract.
    4. Take no further action as the behaviors manifested by the client are consistent with left ventricular failure.

77. Mr. Currie has a 10 00 hours oral antibiotic ordered. The porter arrives at 09 30 hours to take him for an x-ray scheduled for 09 45 hours. Which one of the following actions should the nurse take to administer the medication?

    1. Wait until Mr. Currie returns at 11 15 hours to administer his antibiotic.
    2. Administer the medication immediately prior to Mr. Currie leaving the ward.
    3. Note on Mr. Currie's chart that the medication was withheld due to his chest x-ray.
    4. Remember to go to the x-ray department to administer Mr. Currie's antibiotic at 10 00 hours.

78. Which one of the following nursing interventions should take priority when the nurse begins a shift?

    1. Assess a 2-year-old admitted with croup.
    2. Check an I.V. on a 16-year-old with gastroenteritis.
    3. Administer a prescribed medication to a 9-month-old.
    4. Start a prescribed continuous gastrostomy tube feeding.

79. Which one of the following nursing actions best reflects the use of therapeutic communication when the nurse interacts with a bedridden adult male client?

    1. Ensure the curtains are drawn around his bed.
    2. Stand close to the bedside to demonstrate caring.
    3. Talk about last night's hockey game to build his trust.
    4. Encourage him to share his thoughts about the reason for admission.

80. A nurse is working in a postpartum unit of a small hospital where visiting hours have been changed from restricted to unrestricted time periods. Which one of the following nursing behaviors would indicate the nurse's readiness to accept this change?

    1. Inform clients about the number of visitors allowed at one time.
    2. Provide the new visiting hours to visitors who inquire.
    3. Schedule nursing care to allow the clients to have some private time with visitors.
    4. Voice concerns to visitors about having to implement nursing care when they are present.

81. Mr. Cook, age 74, has been admitted to the hospital for assessment of chronic fatigue. How should the nurse modify the initial assessment to demonstrate an awareness of Mr. Cook's health situation?

    1. Alter the initial assessment to several briefer assessments.
    2. Postpone the nursing assessment until Mr. Cook is feeling stronger.
    3. Listen patiently while Mr. Cook reminisces and talks about his family.
    4. Inform Mr. Cook that when the assessment is finished, he can have a rest.

82. When developing the plan of care for a client, how should the nurse establish expected outcomes?

    1. Complete a thorough assessment of the client.
    2. Evaluate the appropriateness of the nursing strategies.
    3. Develop nursing diagnoses that are specific to the individual client.
    4. Identify client behaviors that will indicate that goals have been met.

83. Upon observing seizure activity in Mrs. Simpson, which one of the following nursing actions should be taken initially?

    1. Set up suction equipment.
    2. Restrain Mrs. Simpson to prevent injury.
    3. Stay with Mrs. Simpson while calling for help.
    4. Reassure Mrs. Simpson by using gentle touch.

84. A nurse has given ascorbic acid 500 mg to a client. When signing for the medication, the nurse notices that the client received 250 mg for the previous dose. On checking the original order the nurse realizes the client was to receive 250 mg b.i.d. What is the most appropriate nursing action?

    1. Inform the nursing supervisor and physician, and take vital signs.
    2. Assess the client for adverse reactions and withhold the next dose.
    3. Inform the nursing supervisor and physician, and fill out an incident report.
    4. Inform the client that the wrong dose was administered and withhold the next dose.

85. Mr. Dougherty, age 68, had a transurethral prostatectomy (TURP) 2 days ago. Which one of the following observations would indicate that Mr. Dougherty is ready for discharge home?

    1. He drank 800 mL of fluid over the past 24 hours.
    2. He tells the nurse that his urine is pink with no clots.
    3. He tells the nurse that he plans to paint his living room this week.
    4. He asks for meperidine hydrochloride (Demerol) before ambulating.

86. Mrs. Raven, age 67, comes from a remote northern village and this is her first hospitalization. An interpreter explains to the nurse that Mrs. Raven is frightened by the voices she hears coming from the wall. The voices are actually coming from the intercom. Which one of the following actions would be most appropriate for the nurse to take to promote Mrs. Raven's psychological safety?

    1. Ensure that everyone speaking to Mrs. Raven faces her directly.
    2. Provide company for Mrs. Raven by moving her to a four-bed room.
    3. Ask the interpreter to explain to Mrs. Raven the purpose of the intercom.
    4. Tell the rest of the staff to speak softly when using the intercom in Mrs. Raven's room.

87. What actions should the nurse take when giving digoxin (Lanoxin) to an 65-year-old client who is currently taking furosemide (Lasix)?

    1. Assess for muscle weakness, visual disturbances, nausea and anorexia indicating digitalis toxicity.

    2. Note signs of dysrhythmias, intestinal colic, tingling and numbness in extremities indicating hyperkalemia.

    3. Observe for increased urinary output, thirst, hypotension and vertigo indicating potentiated effects of the diuretic.

    4. Check for decreased urinary output, hypertension, headaches and edema of feet indicating decreased effectiveness of the diuretic.

88. A nurse has returned to work on a pediatric unit following parental leave. The nurse discovers that while absent there have been many changes in nursing care policies and procedures. Which of the following actions should the nurse take to update competence?

    1. Review new procedures with physicians as they are ordered.

    2. Discuss any changes in nursing care policy with nursing colleagues.

    3. Attend an educational conference on contemporary practice in pediatric nursing.

    4. Participate in developing new policies to ensure understanding of changes in nursing care.

89. Mrs. Dubinski, age 76, is being discharged from hospital following a total replacement of her right hip. Which one of the following actions should the nurse take to plan for a discharge that is compatible with the client's lifestyle?

    1. Teach the client's family about positioning and transferring techniques.

    2. Find out what types of resources are available to the client and her family.

    3. Arrange for a community health nurse to visit the client at home on a regular basis.

    4. Interview family members to determine their availability for providing home care for the client.

90. Which one of the following symptoms would indicate a medication interaction when a 65-year-old male client is receiving lithium carbonate (Lithium) and indomethacin (Indocin/Indocid)?

    1. Thyroid enlargement

    2. Polyuria and polydipsia

    3. Lithium plasma levels of 3 mEq/L

    4. Lithium plasma levels of 0.2 mEq/L

91. Mrs. Watson, age 54, confides to the nurse who is changing her dressing that another nurse was very "rough" while bathing her. As a client advocate, which one of the following interventions is the most appropriate initial action by the nurse?

1. Offer to provide all the care for Mrs. Watson.
2. Observe the other nurse closely to determine if this behavior is repeated.
3. Discuss Mrs. Watson's concerns with the other nurse and clarify the incident.
4. Document the incident fully and submit the documentation to the nursing supervisor.

92. The nurse is admitting a client for surgery. Which one of the following actions should the nurse take as the initial step in planning nursing care?

1. Write a plan for the preoperative nursing care.
2. Have the client do a return demonstration of leg exercises.
3. Review the preoperative checklist and verify its completion.
4. Determine the client's understanding of the proposed surgery.

93. Which one of the following interventions should the nurse perform when administering a gastrostomy tube feeding?

1. Infuse normal saline before the feeding.
2. Elevate the head of the bed a minimum of 30°.
3. Auscultate the lungs to check the position of the tube.
4. Heat the feeding solution to body temperature before infusing it.

94. The morning that Mrs. Goldstein, age 84, is due to be discharged from hospital with her diabetes under control, she stops eating and refuses her insulin. The nurse decides to hold Mrs. Goldstein's discharge and complete a further assessment. Which one of the following statements provides the best rationale for the nurse's plan of care?

1. The diabetic teaching nurse should be consulted for further teaching on diet and insulin.
2. Although Mrs. Goldstein's diabetes is under control, her psychological status needs to be reevaluated.
3. Before discharging Mrs. Goldstein, arrangements need to be made for some nursing follow-up at home.
4. Mrs. Goldstein will need to have her blood sugar monitored as long as she refuses to eat and take her insulin.

95. Which one of the following electrolyte disturbances is likely to predispose a client to digoxin (Lanoxin) toxicity?

1. Hypernatremia
2. Hypochloremia
3. Hypokalemia
4. Hyponatremia

96. The goal for Mr. DiCarlo is: "The client will self-administer b.i.d. medications safely upon discharge." What statement by the client indicates that this goal has been met?

1. "I will take all my pills with milk in the morning."
2. "I have made myself a checklist to sign at every dose."
3. "If I forget one dose, I will take two doses the next time."
4. "My daughter has carefully written down all the information about my medications."

97. The following data relate to an adult female client:

- has a dry cough;
- has smoked one pack of cigarettes a day for the last 10 years;
- is currently a smoker;
- has had stress incontinence for the past 5 years; and
- has used Kegel exercises b.i.d. for the past 5 years.

Which one of the following nursing entries conveys the client information in the most concise and organized manner?

1. States she has a cough and is a smoker; has a history of stress incontinence.
2. States she has a dry cough and smokes (1 pack per day X 10 years). History of stress incontinence X 5 years; uses Kegel exercises b.i.d.
3. States she has a dry cough and uses Kegel exercises b.i.d. Smokes (1 pack per day X 10 years). Has a history of stress incontinence X 5 years.
4. States she has a dry cough but uses Kegel exercises b.i.d. She smokes (1 pack per day X 10 years), and relates a history of stress incontinence for the past 5 years.

98. Which one of the following actions is the most effective way for nurses to practice ongoing self-evaluation?

1. Seek peer-evaluation on a regular basis.
2. Write out weaknesses and develop plans to overcome them.
3. Reflect on their performance as caregivers and determine areas for growth.
4. Meet with their nursing supervisor on an annual basis to evaluate their individual performance.

99.   Mrs. Gomez and her daughter return to the Geriatric Assessment Unit for a review of Mrs. Gomez's medications. What should the nurse do initially to assess Mrs. Gomez's current status?

       1.   Ask Mrs. Gomez about her medications.
       2.   Ask her daughter about Mrs. Gomez's medications.
       3.   Look at Mrs. Gomez's chart to see what was prescribed.
       4.   Check the referral note from the community health nurse.

100. What should the nurse do upon discovering a nursing colleague who disagrees on technique regarding the administration of an I.V. medication?

       1.   Call the physician and report the situation.
       2.   Discuss the situation with other colleagues.
       3.   Ask the pharmacist to speak to the colleague.
       4.   Consult a drug reference book with the colleague.

END OF INDEPENDENT ITEMS

CASE 9

Mr. Joser Ali is a 65-year-old man who is married and the father of two grown children. Following a history of urinary problems, a radical prostatectomy is indicated for removal of a stage I tumor. Mr. Ali is a devout Muslim.

ITEMS 101 to 106 refer to this case.

101. The nurse determines that Mr. Ali, who has already signed his surgical consent, does not understand the implications of having a radical prostatectomy. What action should the nurse take?

       1.   Review the consent form with him.
       2.   Inform him of the implications of the surgery.
       3.   Teach him about the role of the prostate in sexual activity.
       4.   Report to the surgeon that he does not understand the surgery.

102. Following preoperative administration of diazepam (Valium) to Mr. Ali, which one of the following actions should the nurse take?

    1. Document his response to the medication.
    2. Observe him for signs of urinary retention.
    3. Reinforce preoperative teaching related to his surgery.
    4. Notify the anesthetist that his medication was administered.

103. On Mr. Ali's second postoperative day, he has an indwelling Foley catheter. Which nursing action should be included in the nursing care plan?

    1. Immediately report blood-tinged urine.
    2. Check the catheter drainage system q. 2h.
    3. Ensure total intake does not exceed 1000 mL every 24 hours.
    4. Clamp the catheter tubing q. 4h to maintain bladder muscle tone.

104. Postoperatively, Mr. Ali requires assistance with washing prior to prayer. This has increased work for the nursing staff, and is raised as an issue at a team meeting. Which one of the following nursing actions demonstrates responsible advocacy?

    1. Contact the social worker to arrange for consultation with a client advocate.
    2. Volunteer to be the primary nurse to assist Mr. Ali with his preparations for prayer.
    3. Represent the client by interpreting and explaining his religious practices to the team.
    4. Consult with the client's wife to ensure that a family member is present to assist with bathing prior to prayer.

105. On Mr. Ali's fourth postoperative day, the catheter is removed. Which one of the following nursing interventions should be documented in his plan of care?

    1. Limit perineal exercises.
    2. Measure volume of voidings.
    3. Record 24-hour intake and output.
    4. Teach intermittent self-catheterization.

106. Mr. Ali is preparing for discharge. How should the nurse determine what Mr. Ali perceives as his needs when he returns home?

    1. Discuss with Mr. Ali his role within the Ali family.
    2. Ask Mr. Ali how he sees the surgery affecting his life.
    3. Explore with Mr. Ali his feelings regarding the diagnosis of cancer.
    4. Assess Mr. Ali's understanding of the postsurgical activity restrictions.

END OF CASE 9

CASE 10

Mrs. Edwards, 76 years old, fractured her right hip in a fall. Three days ago, Mrs. Edwards underwent repair of an intertrochanteric fracture with a plate and screws. She is to mobilize, but due to considerable pain, is reluctant to get out of bed.

ITEMS 107 TO 112 refer to this case.

107. During her postoperative recovery, Mrs. Edwards is encouraged to deep breathe to improve her respiratory status. Because of Mrs. Edwards' age, what information should the nurse consider in carrying out this intervention?
    1. The airways remain essentially the same size throughout life.
    2. Coughing while ambulating will stimulate expectoration.
    3. Mrs. Edwards' breathing will be more rapid and shallow than that of a younger person.
    4. With exercise, Mrs. Edwards will be able to expand her lungs to a size similar to those of a younger person.

108. Mrs. Edwards has difficulty voiding postoperatively. There is an order for intermittent catheterization p.r.n. When should Mrs. Edwards be catheterized?
    1. When her bladder becomes distended.
    2. After she has unsuccessfully attempted to void.
    3. Every 3-4 hours, whether or not she is able to void on her own.
    4. Every 6-8 hours to enable the client to void between catheterizations.

109. Mrs. Edwards is encouraged to mobilize. However, the client states that her hip is painful when she stands and walks. The medication order reads: acetaminophen and codeine (Tylenol #2), 1-2 tablets, p.o., q. 4-6h, p.r.n. To increase Mrs. Edwards' comfort when mobilizing, which one of the following actions should the nurse take when calculating Mrs. Edwards' medication dosage ?
    1. Halve the dosage because of her age.
    2. Take into account her present weight.
    3. Assess her degree of pain based on her ability to mobilize.
    4. Give her the full p.r.n. dosage as prescribed by the physician.

110. What information concerning mobilization is the most essential to document in Mrs. Edwards' plan of care?

    1. The footwear and type of walker to use
    2. The side of the bed from which to assist the client
    3. The frequency and length of time the client may mobilize
    4. The amount of weight the client is able to bear on her leg

111. On her fourth postoperative day, Mrs. Edwards states that she is constipated and has not moved her bowels since her fall. Laxatives and a high-fibre diet have not been effective. Which one of the following precautions should the nurse take when performing disimpaction?

    1. Remove hard stool until the client begins to evacuate stool on her own.
    2. Attempt to remove large pieces of stool so the procedure is not prolonged.
    3. Remove feces gently so as to minimize the risk of stimulating the vagus nerve.
    4. Advise the client to hold her breath at intervals to reduce the discomfort of the procedure.

112. Seven days postsurgery, the nurse is finalizing discharge planning for Mrs. Edwards' home care. How should the nurse best assist Mrs. Edwards with her discharge?

    1. Include Mrs. Edwards in all aspects of her discharge planning.
    2. Give a family member the required information to arrange for home care services.
    3. Assure Mrs. Edwards that the necessary agencies have been contacted about her discharge.
    4. Provide the names and telephone numbers of appropriate home care agencies for Mrs. Edwards to call.

END OF CASE 10

CASE 11

Mrs. Huang is a 73-year-old client admitted for a lumpectomy of the right breast. She lives with her son and daughter-in-law. She speaks only a few words of English.

ITEMS 113 to 118 refer to this case.

113. The nurse meets with Mrs. Huang upon admission to conduct the initial assessment and interview but Mrs. Huang does not respond to the nurse's questions. What is the most probable conclusion the nurse should make about this behavior?
    1. Mrs. Huang has a hearing loss.
    2. Mrs. Huang is experiencing preoperative anxiety.
    3. Mrs. Huang does not understand the nurse's questions.
    4. Mrs. Huang does not want to be interviewed at this time.

114. Mrs. Huang is scheduled for surgery at 09 30 hours. She is to receive lorazepam (Ativan) 1 mg sublingually, one hour preoperatively. What initial action should the nurse implement in administering this medication?
    1. Check the medication record.
    2. Clarify the order with the physician.
    3. Crush the tablet before administration.
    4. Check the client's chart for the original order.

115. In administering medication to Mrs. Huang, which one of the following safety measures should the nurse use in identifying the client?
    1. Ask the client to identify herself.
    2. Check the name label on the bed.
    3. Ask the client if she is Mrs. Huang.
    4. Check the client's identification bracelet.

116. In the immediate postoperative phase, which one of the following interventions would best assist Mrs. Huang to perform deep breathing exercises?
    1. Demonstrate the technique to the client and have her perform it.
    2. Leave written instructions for the exercises at the client's bedside.
    3. Point to the incentive spirometer and place it in the client's hand.
    4. Ask Mrs. Huang to perform the exercises as she was instructed preoperatively.

117. When is it appropriate for the nurse to discontinue Mrs. Huang's intravenous in the postoperative period?

    1. Upon her return to the unit
    2. When she tolerates oral fluids
    3. When her surgical dressing is dry
    4. Eight hours after her return to the unit

118. After Mrs. Huang is discharged, the primary nurse evaluates the care given to this client and realizes that there were barriers to optimal nursing care because of cultural differences. Which one of the following actions should the nursing team take to enhance nursing care in the future?

    1. Seek the help of a translator to create a glossary of common phrases in Mrs. Huang's language.
    2. Explore literature that pertains to the nursing of clients from different cultural backgrounds.
    3. Use knowledge and skills attained from this nurse-client relationship in future situations with similar clients.
    4. Create a standard care plan relating to Mrs. Huang's cultural background which can be used in the future with similar clients.

END OF CASE 11

INDEPENDENT ITEMS

ITEMS 119 to 129 do not refer to a case.

119. Mr. Howard has sustained a depressed skull fracture and is comatose. Which one of the following assessments by the nurse would best indicate an increasing intracranial pressure?

    1. His pulse is increasing.
    2. His temperature is decreasing.
    3. His systolic blood pressure is increasing.
    4. He withdraws his legs in response to a pinprick.

120. The nurse returns from break to find that the status of two clients has deteriorated significantly. The nurse now needs to assess their vital signs every 15 minutes and administer several stat. medications. In addition, a third client requires insulin. In evaluating this situation, which one of the following conclusions should the nurse make?

    1. The present workload is unrealistic for the nurse to manage.
    2. The nurse does not have enough knowledge to manage this situation.
    3. The nurse needs to reprioritize the nursing care plans for each of the clients.
    4. The nurse should administer the insulin first to free time to attend to the clients who are acutely ill.

121. Mrs. Jones, age 64, has rheumatoid arthritis. She has been admitted for adjustment of her nonsteroidal anti-inflammatory medication and a mobilization program. Which one of the following sequences of events is most appropriate for Mrs. Jones upon awakening?

    1. Breakfast, anti-inflammatory medications, a hot shower, and physiotherapy
    2. Anti-inflammatory medications, breakfast, physiotherapy, and a hot shower
    3. Breakfast, physiotherapy, anti-inflammatory medications, and a hot shower
    4. A hot shower, breakfast, physiotherapy, and anti-inflammatory medications

122. Mrs. Thornton, age 48, is admitted for surgery. She has been profoundly visually impaired since birth and functions independently. Mrs. Thornton was placed in bed with the side rails up. What should the nurse do to lessen Mrs. Thornton's obvious distress with these restrictions?

    1. Lower the side rails and allow Mrs. Thornton to move around at will.
    2. Sit with Mrs. Thornton until she becomes accustomed to the side rails.
    3. Lower the side rails and orient Mrs. Thornton to her new environment.
    4. Explain to Mrs. Thornton why she must remain in bed with the side rails up.

123. Mrs. Chan arrives at the obstetrical unit in labor. On admission, she requests that an episiotomy be avoided if at all possible. During second stage labor, the physician becomes impatient with the fetal descent despite adequate progress and plans for a forceps delivery with an episiotomy. Which one of the following actions should the nurse take in the role of client advocate?

    1. Prepare the equipment for Mrs. Chan's forceps delivery.
    2. Explore Mrs. Chan's understanding of the need for an episiotomy.
    3. Negotiate with the physician to allow Mrs. Chan to continue with unassisted pushing.
    4. Tell Mrs. Chan to remind her physician that she had requested not to have an episiotomy.

124. Which intervention by the nurse would demonstrate active listening during the initial interview with a client?

    1. Maintaining eye contact
    2. Sitting with arms crossed
    3. Sitting quietly, recording the information
    4. Responding quickly to the client's comments

125. A nurse assigned to the care of 9-year-old Benjamin, 2 days postappendectomy, finds him in a fetal position, moaning, and guarding his lower abdomen. Further assessment reveals diaphoresis, P 115 beats/min, and BP 110/80 mmHg. When the nurse asks Benjamin if he feels any pain, he responds, "No, none at all." He was prescribed codeine I.M., q. 3-4h, p.r.n. which was last administered 3 hours ago. Which one of the following interventions by the nurse is most appropriate?

    1. Return to the medication room to prepare the prescribed medication.
    2. Sit with Benjamin in an effort to determine why he appears to be upset.
    3. Wait for Benjamin's mother to arrive to help in the assessment of Benjamin's discomfort.
    4. Remind Benjamin of the importance of reporting his discomfort to the nurse and proceed with other aspects of his care.

126. Mr. Woods, 65 years old, has just been admitted to the unit in respiratory distress. To collect the appropriate data, which one of the following actions should the nurse take first?

    1. Take his vital signs.
    2. Complete the nursing admission.
    3. Review his previous medical records.
    4. Consult with the respiratory technologist.

127. Mrs. Fuller, an 86-year-old, has been admitted to hospital for evaluation of her frequent fainting episodes. During the night, she hits her head when she falls in the bathroom. Which one of the following nursing actions would best indicate that the nurse has effectively intervened when Mrs. Fuller is found?

    1. Assess the client's neurological and vital signs.
    2. Restrain the client in a chair at the nurses' station.
    3. Make the client comfortable and encourage her to rest.
    4. Complete the incident report form within 1 hour of the fall.

128. Four-year-old Nancy is brought into the emergency department by her father. He reports that while playing on the bed, Nancy fell and bumped her head. After observing a large hematoma on Nancy's forehead, and bruising on her legs and buttocks in various stages of healing, the nurse suspects that Nancy has been physically abused. Which one of the following actions should the nurse take?

1. Report the suspicions to the local police.
2. Ask Nancy's father to wait outside the examining room.
3. Confer with the emergency department physician and social worker.
4. Contact Nancy's mother and request that she come immediately to the emergency department.

129. Mrs. Martin, 72 years old, is hospitalized for a burn to her abdomen. Which one of the following actions should the nurse take to ensure that Mrs. Martin is able to care for her burn at home?

1. Refer her to the hospital's home care department.
2. Observe her performing a sterile dressing change.
3. Give her a list of resources she can call for assistance.
4. Provide her with a teaching video on sterile dressings.

END OF INDEPENDENT ITEMS

END OF BOOK 1

Canadian Nurses Association

Testing division

Nurse Registration/Licensure Examination

CANDIDATE NUMBER

SIGNATURE

Book 2
Test Form 5208

READ THE INSTRUCTIONS AND SAMPLE ITEMS INSIDE THE FRONT COVER

CANADIAN NURSES ASSOCIATION
ASSOCIATION DES INFIRMIÈRES ET INFIRMIERS DU CANADA

INSTRUCTIONS

A) TESTING TIME AND MATERIAL

You will have three and one-half hours to work on this test. The starting and finishing times will be announced and you will be advised when there are 30 and 15 minutes working time remaining. If at any time you have any questions about what you should do, raise your hand and an invigilator will assist you.

You will be advised whether you may leave the examination room if you finish the test before the time is up. You must *stop* working when the signal is given. An invigilator will check your test book and answer sheet *before* you leave.

Clear your desk of all materials except your identification card, response sheet, test book, pencils, and eraser. Do *not* fold, bend, or tear your answer sheet, as this could affect the scoring of your test.

B) ANSWER SHEET

Use the diagram on the back cover of your test book as a guide for filling in the boxes in the identification portion of your answer sheet. Fill in your CANDIDATE NUMBER, the WRITING CENTRE CODE, and the TEST FORM by following the instructions on the answer sheet. If you do not have a candidate number leave this section blank. Complete the box headed LANGUAGE OF WRITING.

Be sure the mark you make for each answer is black, fills the oval, and contains the number corresponding to the number of the answer you have chosen. Do *not* fill in more than one oval for an item or you will get no credit for it. Erase *completely* any answer you wish to change and mark your new choice in the correct oval. An incomplete erasure may be read incorrectly as an intended answer. Do not press too heavily on your pencil or you may damage the answer sheet.

Note that the items on the answer sheet are numbered in columns. There are fewer items in the test book than there are numbers on the answer sheet.

Make no stray marks on the response sheet; they may count against you. You may use the margins of the test book for any scratch work, but you will *not* get credit for anything you write in the test book.

C) TEST BOOKLET

Sign your name on the line on the cover of this booklet and copy your candidate number into the appropriate boxes. If you do not have a candidate number, *print* your name under your signature.

Read each item or question carefully and choose the answer you think is *correct*. If you cannot decide on an answer to an item, go on to the next one and come back to this item later if you have time. Try to answer all items. Marks are not subtracted for wrong answers. If you are not sure of an answer, it will be to your advantage to guess. It will probably be best to start at the beginning of the test and work through the items in order.

This examination contains a number of experimental items being tested for future use. Your answers to these items will *not* count toward your score. Because you will not be able to tell which items are experimental, you should do your best on all items, but do *not* spend too much time on any item.

The items in the examination may be presented in nursing cases. The context of some cases may seem similar to others in your test book. This reflects current practice where a nurse may have to care for different clients with similar problems. Each case, however, tests different nursing content. The sample case on the next page shows the types of items used. Correct answers are blackened in the ovals on the right.

NOTE: Wherever the feminine is used, it shall be construed as referring also to the masculine if the context so requires.

SAMPLE CASE

Mr. Robert Lowry, an 82-year-old married man, collapses at home. Mr. Lowry is rushed to the community hospital where it is determined that he has suffered a cerebrovascular accident (CVA). Mrs. Lowry tells the nurse that, prior to this incident, her husband had been taking a thiazide diuretic to control his hypertension.

ITEMS 1 to 5 refer to this case.

1. Which of the following initial nursing assessments would determine Mr. Lowry's level of consciousness?

   1. Visual fields
   2. Auditory acuity
   3. Deep tendon reflexes
   4. Responses to painful stimuli   ①②③●

2. Mr. Lowry regains consciousness and is found to have loss of movement on his left side and hemianopsia. Which one of the following responses by the nurse would be appropriate to give Mrs. Lowry when she asks questions regarding her husband's potential for recovery?

   1. "It's difficult to know, but most people take at least a year to recover completely."
   2. "It sounds as though you may be somewhat anxious to resume your former lifestyle."   ①②●④
   3. "Concern about recovery is common. Rehabilitation takes time and progress is often slow."
   4. "To be anxious is normal. Unfortunately, there is no way of estimating your husband's recovery potential."

3. Mr. Lowry is receiving a thiazide diuretic. Which one of the following manifestations would indicate mild hypokalemia?

   1. Anorexia
   2. Bradycardia
   3. Muscle spasms   ●②③④
   4. Elevated blood pressure

4. Which of the following interventions should the nurse implement to encourage Mr. Lowry to feed himself?

   1. Assist him to position the cutlery in his hands.
   2. Suggest that Mrs. Lowry take him to the cafeteria.
   3. Arrange food items on his tray so he can see them.   ①②●④
   4. Allow sufficient time for him to cut up his own food.

5. Which one of the following nursing observations of Mrs. Lowry's behavior would best indicate her readiness to participate in her husband's care at home?

   1. She visits him every day.
   2. She selects his daily menus.
   3. She brings his shaving kit and pyjamas from home.   ①②③●
   4. She asks if she is correctly positioned to help him walk.

END OF SAMPLE CASE

DO NOT OPEN YOUR TEST BOOK OR BEGIN WORKING UNTIL THE SIGNAL IS GIVEN TO DO SO

CASE 12

Mr. Juliano, a 73-year-old man, has just been admitted to the medical unit with an exacerbation of his chronic congestive heart failure. He states that he is having more trouble breathing today and did not sleep well last night.

ITEMS 1 to 6 refer to this case.

1. Mr. Juliano's respirations become labored. Prior to the physician's arrival, which one of the following actions should the nurse take first?
    1. Place him in high-Fowler's position.
    2. Start O_2 at 8 L/min using a Venturi mask.
    3. Prepare the equipment to start an intravenous infusion.
    4. Arrange for the lab to draw blood for blood gas analysis.

2. Mr. Juliano is receiving O_2 by Venturi mask. Which one of the following actions should the nurse take to promote a safe environment while this therapy is being carried out?
    1. Replace cotton blankets with polyester ones.
    2. Remove electrical equipment from the room.
    3. Check that the ports on the mask are unobstructed.
    4. Avoid using oil-based creams when providing skin care.

3. Mr. Juliano is receiving therapy with digoxin (Lanoxin). Which one of the following client characteristics must the nurse record when giving the medication?
    1. Heart rate
    2. Blood pressure
    3. Respiratory rate
    4. Level of activity

4. Which one of the following factors would contribute most to Mr. Juliano experiencing sensory overload?
    1. His intravenous rate is checked hourly.
    2. His wife visits regularly, each afternoon.
    3. The drapes are drawn to block strong sunlight.
    4. The oxygen humidification unit gurgles continuously.

5. On the third day following Mr. Juliano's admission, which one of the following observations would be most important to include in the report to the incoming shift of nursing staff?

    1. His weight continues to remain stable.
    2. He is dizzy when he first gets out of bed.
    3. He needs reminders to keep his feet elevated.
    4. He has been sleeping for short periods at regular intervals.

6. During the evening shift, Mr. Juliano's condition worsens. The physician orders his transfer to the cardiac care unit, but there are no beds available. One nurse goes home sick, leaving one nurse and one practical nurse/nursing assistant on the unit to care for 20 clients. Which one of the following factors should be most important to the nurse in determining if this is an unrealistic workload?

    1. Number of hours remaining in the shift
    2. Complexity of care required by the clients
    3. Administrative tasks which need completion
    4. Degree of experience of the practical nurse/nursing assistant

END OF CASE 12

CASE 13

Mrs. Peters is an 85-year-old widow who has been hospitalized following a hip fracture. She is frail and anorexic. Nasogastric feeding is initiated.

ITEMS 7 to 12 refer to this case.

7. Which one of the following nursing diagnoses best reflects the nursing assessment data?

    1. Anxiety related to hospitalization
    2. Altered nutrition related to poor appetite
    3. Constipation related to nasogastric feeding
    4. Fluid volume deficit related to nasogastric feeding

8. Which initial intervention should the nurse perform before feeding Mrs. Peters via a nasogastric tube?

    1. Check for placement of the tube.
    2. Place the client in the left lateral position.
    3. Change the tubing before each feeding.
    4. Instill 60 mL of water through the tube.

GO TO NEXT PAGE

9. Which one of the following nursing interventions would best promote sensory stimulation for Mrs. Peters?

    1. Move her to the activity room.
    2. Remove photos of family members.
    3. Place a clock and calendar in her room.
    4. Talk with her while assisting her with her care.

10. Mrs. Peters becomes confused and refuses to allow the nurse to treat her. She says to the nurse, "Who are you? Leave me alone." Which one of the following revisions should the nurse make to the plan of care?

    1. Monitor her orientation status.
    2. Provide sedation as necessary.
    3. Encourage the client to express her concerns.
    4. Encourage the client to participate in the plan of care.

11. The nurse finds it increasingly difficult to care for Mrs. Peters. What should the nurse do to cope with feelings of frustration?

    1. Maintain high-quality care at all times.
    2. Decrease the amount of time spent with the client.
    3. Consult a nursing colleague regarding Mrs. Peters' care.
    4. Insist that another nurse assume the care for the client.

12. Mrs. Peters' condition worsens and it becomes difficult to maintain a clear airway. The nurse promotes ventilation and respiration by performing oral and nasal suctioning. Which one of the following interventions indicates safe technique in suctioning Mrs. Peters?

    1. Suction the oral cavity first.
    2. Suction for as long as necessary.
    3. Insert the catheter without applying suction.
    4. Place the client in a lateral position facing the nurse.

END OF CASE 13

CASE 14

Kyle Landon, age 14, lives with his single mother. He has been referred to an outpatient clinic because of suicidal ideation.

ITEMS 13 to 18 refer to this case.

13. Which one of the following responses should the nurse make when Kyle states, "I'm not talking to you. You're just like all the other grown-ups who keep bugging me"?
    1. "Do you feel like other adults are against you?"
    2. "I'd like to hear more about what you are feeling."
    3. "I'll be happy to come back when you feel like talking."
    4. "How can you know that I will be like other grown-ups in your life?"

14. An interview with Kyle reveals that he is a classmate of the nurse's son, David. What should the nurse do to ensure confidentiality?
    1. Refrain from discussing any aspect of Kyle's care with David.
    2. Inform the health care team that another nurse should care for Kyle.
    3. Ask David not to discuss Kyle's suicidal behaviors with his classmates.
    4. Report to Kyle's principal, in confidence, that Kyle is making good progress.

15. What should the nurse do when Kyle refuses to attend his prescribed group therapy sessions?
    1. Encourage Kyle to verbalize his reasons for refusing to attend group therapy.
    2. Inform Kyle that it is in his best interest to comply with the prescribed treatment plan.
    3. Discuss Kyle's refusal with his mother and solicit her help to encourage him to attend.
    4. Tell Kyle that he would probably enjoy the special activity the group has planned for today.

16. What should the nurse do when several colleagues suggest that Kyle's plan of care would be more effective if his mother were more actively involved?

    1. Explore further the colleagues' suggestion and consider how to incorporate it into the plan of care.

    2. Listen respectfully to the colleagues' criticism and then continue with the health care team's established plan of care.

    3. Recognize a personal weakness in psychiatric nursing skills and seek out learning opportunities to develop these skills.

    4. Point out to these colleagues that Kyle's mother has limited resources and should not be expected to be more involved in his care.

17. How should the nurse determine the level of satisfaction Kyle and his mother have with the nursing care provided?

    1. Request that Kyle and his mother complete an agency survey regarding client satisfaction.

    2. Throughout Kyle's care, seek feedback on their satisfaction with the individual nurses at the agency.

    3. Collect data from the health care team and Kyle's mother regarding any further evidence of suicidal ideation.

    4. During the discharge interview with Kyle and his mother, determine if all mutually agreed upon goals have been met.

18. How should the nurse coordinate Kyle's care plan to ensure continuity of care while the nurse is on vacation?

    1. Assure Kyle that the other nurses are aware of his needs and are well-qualified to help him.

    2. Arrange for Kyle to be admitted to hospital during the nurse's absence so that he can be closely monitored.

    3. Discuss the treatment plan and the progress made with Kyle, his mother, and the health care team prior to leaving.

    4. Validate with Kyle and his mother that they will be able to follow through on the treatment plan during the nurse's absence.

END OF CASE 14

CASE 15

Mr. Collier is a 32-year-old client with end-stage Acquired Immune Deficiency Syndrome (AIDS). Because his partner is no longer able to care for him at home, Mr. Collier is admitted to a facility for respite care.

ITEMS 19 to 24 refer to this case.

19. Which one of the following factors would most likely be detrimental to Mr. Collier's psychological well-being?

    1. Post-test HIV counseling
    2. Central nervous system changes
    3. Blood and body fluid precautions
    4. Facility policies regarding documentation

20. Mr. Collier's partner states, "Even though I tested negative before, I'm still worried I have AIDS." Which one of the following nursing actions would be most appropriate?

    1. Refer the partner to a sex therapist.
    2. Give the partner information on safer sex.
    3. Clarify with the partner the reason for the concern.
    4. Explore with the partner the details of their sexual history.

21. Which one of the following nursing interventions would promote adequate oral fluid intake for Mr. Collier?

    1. Encourage Mr. Collier to drink hot beverages.
    2. Instruct Mr. Collier to select mild drinks such as apple juice.
    3. Instruct Mr. Collier how to record his oral fluids on the intake and output sheet.
    4. Explain to Mr. Collier that total parenteral nutrition may be required if his oral intake is inadequate.

22. Which one of the following nursing actions would promote Mr. Collier's comfort when he is lying in bed?

    1. Place a foot board on his bed.
    2. Support his limbs with pillows.
    3. Obtain assistance to log roll him.
    4. Teach him to use an overhead trapeze bar.

23. Which one of the following nursing actions would encourage Mr. Collier to maintain his optimum activity level?

    1. Teach Mr. Collier's partner safe transferring techniques.
    2. Teach Mr. Collier how to perform isometric exercises q. 8h.
    3. Assist Mr. Collier to perform range-of-motion exercises as tolerated.
    4. Involve the occupational therapist in teaching Mr. Collier about activities of daily living.

24. Mr. Collier develops pneumonia and his physician prescribes an antibiotic. When the nurse prepares to administer this medication, Mr. Collier states, "No way! I'm not taking any more stuff." Which one of the following nursing actions would be appropriate at this time?

    1. Try administering the medication to Mr. Collier at a later time.
    2. Explore with Mr. Collier his reasons for refusing the treatment.
    3. Ask Mr. Collier's partner to explain the importance of treatment.
    4. Withhold the medication and immediately notify Mr. Collier's physician.

END OF CASE 15

CASE 16

Jane Brown is a 3-month-old child who is admitted to the pediatric unit for evaluation. Her presenting symptoms are weight loss and irritability. Jane is diagnosed as having nonorganic failure to thrive. Her parents are young and inexperienced with childrearing.

ITEMS 25 to 29 refer to this case.

25. Which one of the following questions should the nurse ask to determine if the parents are facilitating Jane's developmental task of "trust," as defined by Erikson?

    1. "What do you do when your baby cries?"
    2. "Do you provide your baby with a pacifier?"
    3. "What types of food do you feed your baby?"
    4. "What types of toys do you provide for your baby?"

26. The initial assessment data reveal that Jane's urinary output is decreased, her anterior fontanel is sunken, and there is a decrease in her skin turgor. Which one of the following conditions is most likely indicated by these findings?

    1. Dehydration
    2. Hypervolemia
    3. Hyponatremia
    4. Water intoxication

27. Which one of the following actions by the nurse would promote Jane's physical safety while she is in the hospital crib?

    1. Elevate Jane's crib sides fully at all times.
    2. Position the crib mobile 15 cm above Jane's face.
    3. Place a bubble top or net on the crib at the time of admission.
    4. Encourage her parents to position Jane with her head on a pillow.

28. Jane's parents state that they are afraid to bathe her because she is so small. Instead, they have just been wiping her with a cloth. What would be the best action by the nurse to promote Jane's hygiene?

    1. Assist the parents to bathe Jane during her hospitalization.
    2. Ensure that Jane is bathed by staff during her hospital stay.
    3. Arrange to have follow-up supervision during Jane's bath time at home.
    4. Have the parents demonstrate the bathing technique they have been using.

29. Which one of the following behaviors by the nurse would best demonstrate a caring attitude toward Jane's parents?

    1. Offer to feed Jane when her parents seem tired.
    2. Recommend that Jane's parents contact the social worker.
    3. Suggest to Jane's parents that they stay with her 24 hours/day.
    4. Offer Jane's parents reading material on effective parenting skills.

END OF CASE 16

CASE 17

Mrs. Maria Signoretti is a 51-year-old woman who has come to the Women's Health Centre because she thinks she may be starting menopause. During the initial meeting with the nurse, Maria states that she wants to know more about pills to control her hot flashes and ways to remain healthy. She also states that she has heard her friends talk about older women developing "brittle bones" and wants to know what she can do to prevent this.

ITEMS 30 to 35 refer to this case.

30. When interviewing Maria, which one of the following psychosocial assessments by the nurse would be most appropriate?

    1. Her religious affiliation and her marital status
    2. Her cultural background and her feelings about aging
    3. Her financial status and her husband's attitude toward her
    4. Her socioeconomic status and the number of children she has had

31. Maria tells the nurse that she has been having hot sweats every day and trouble sleeping at night. She has not had a menstrual period for 3 months, and states that she does not enjoy sexual relations now because it is painful and she is afraid of becoming pregnant. Which one of the following entries into the nursing notes is most appropriate?

    1. Amenorrhea for 3 months, fearful of becoming pregnant, complains of insomnia, painful coitus, hot flashes
    2. Amenorrhea for 3 months, hot flashes daily, insomnia, developing frigidity related to painful intercourse and fear of pregnancy
    3. Amenorrhea for 3 months, hot flashes daily, loss of pleasure with coitus associated with dyspareunia and fear of pregnancy, insomnia
    4. Amenorrhea for 3 months, anxious regarding conception, complains of insomnia, painful coitus, hot flashes, fears becoming pregnant

32. Maria states that at one time she found sexual relations pleasurable, but now she finds intercourse painful. Which one of the following statements is the most appropriate nursing diagnosis?

    1. Anxiety related to changing body image
    2. Knowledge deficit related to changes in sexual patterns
    3. Altered self-esteem related to changes in sexual patterns
    4. Sexual dysfunction related to hormonal changes of menopause

33.   The physician has ordered transdermal estrogen replacement therapy for Maria. After 2 months she makes a follow-up visit to the Women's Health Centre. To assess Maria's response to the medication, which one of the following statements by the nurse would be most appropriate?

      1.   "Have you had any side effects from the patch?"
      2.   "How do you feel since you started using the patch?"
      3.   "Has the patch controlled the problems you were having?"
      4.   "Are you feeling better since you started using the patch?"

34.   The nurse has developed an osteoporosis education plan with Maria. Which one of the following principles is most important for the nurse to apply when implementing the plan?

      1.   The client must be ready to learn.
      2.   A follow-up session with oral questioning will assist in evaluation.
      3.   The teaching materials must be at the client's comprehension level.
      4.   The client should be asked what she already knows about osteoporosis.

35.   The nurse scheduled to care for Maria is new to the Women's Health Centre. How should this nurse prepare to care for Maria?

      1.   Collect teaching pamphlets on menopause.
      2.   Attend a workshop on aging and menopause.
      3.   Talk to a co-worker who is going through menopause.
      4.   Ask Maria to share what she has learned about menopause.

END OF CASE 17

CASE 18

Mr. Stan James, age 45, has returned to a surgical unit following a hiatus hernia repair. His chart states that he is moderately developmentally delayed.

ITEMS 36 to 41 refer to this case.

36. The nurse assesses that Mr. James has a very low tolerance for pain. How should the nurse sequence interventions for Mr. James when he requires several painful procedures?

　　→1. Give I.M. injection of analgesic, rest for 20 minutes, set up I.V. for blood transfusion, insert Foley catheter
　　　2. Allow rest period, insert Foley catheter, give I.M. injection of analgesic, set up I.V. for blood transfusion
　　　3. Set up I.V. for blood transfusion, insert Foley catheter, give I.M. injection of analgesic, maintain on bedrest
　　　4. Insert Foley catheter, give I.M. injection of analgesic, set up I.V. for blood transfusion, encourage rest when all interventions are completed

37. The nurse assesses Mr. James and decides to administer dimenhydrate (Gravol) 25 mg I.M. which the physician has ordered to be administered q. 4h, p.r.n. This drug is dispensed in 5 mL vials containing 250 mg. What would be the correct volume for the nurse to administer to Mr. James?

　　　1. 0.05 mL
　　　2. 0.25 mL
　　　3. 0.50 mL
　　　4. 2.50 mL

$$\frac{DD}{DH} \times R \qquad \frac{25mg}{250mg} \times 5ml =$$

38. Mr. James has a #16 indwelling urinary catheter in place. The nurse notes that there has been 35 mL of urinary output in the past hour, whereas the previous hourly rate had been approximately 70 mL. Which of the following actions should the nurse take initially?

　　　1. Remove the catheter and replace it with one of a larger size.
　　　2. Irrigate the catheter using a large volume syringe and sterile solution.
　　　3. Disconnect the catheter from the drainage bag to check for urinary flow.
　　　4. Check the catheter and drainage tubing for kinks that might impede flow.

39. Following surgery, Mr. James is to receive three units of packed red blood cells. How should the nurse maintain the transfusion?

    1. Ensure the transfusion is maintained at a constant flow rate.

    2. Regulate the infusion to the slowest possible rate to avoid transfusion reactions.

    3. Infuse the blood slowly for the first 15 minutes, then increase the flow rate to that ordered by the physician.

    4. Administer the transfusion as quickly as possible by using a pressure appliance on each unit of packed red blood cells.

40. Which one of the following actions by the nurse would best ensure Mr. James' safety?

    1. Have a relative remain with him.

    2. Supervise him when he performs activities.

    3. Place him in a four-bed room after explaining his status to the other clients in the room.

    4. Place a sign above his bed that would indicate to all staff that he needs special supervision.

41. Postoperatively, Mr. James has been having small, liquid bowel movements frequently. The nurse assesses that he has a large amount of hard feces in his rectum. How should the nurse deal with Mr. James' problem?

    1. Request an order for a saline enema.

    2. Administer the prescribed laxative every night.

    3. Ask him what method he usually uses to correct constipation.

    4. Insert a lubricated, gloved finger into the rectum and break up the fecal mass.

END OF CASE 18

CASE 19

Mrs. Smith, a 69-year-old client with Parkinson's disease, is experiencing difficulties with activities of daily living because of increasing motor dysfunction. She has been admitted to a geriatric assessment unit for functional assessment and health teaching. Mrs. Smith's husband and daughter are attending the teaching sessions with her.

ITEMS 42 to 47 refer to this case.

42. What is the most important reason for the nurse to discuss the nursing diagnoses with Mrs. Smith and her family?

    1. To ensure that the client's needs are addressed
    2. To help Mrs. Smith's family with skills to assist her when she returns home
    3. To provide the emotional support necessary for the family to continue in the caregiving role
    4. To allow for interaction among the client, family, and nurse, which is important for Mrs. Smith's well-being

43. Which one of the following nursing diagnoses is most relevant to the needs of Mrs. Smith and her family?

    1. Ineffective coping related to depression
    2. Activity intolerance related to motor dysfunction
    3. Self-care deficit related to tremor and motor disturbance
    4. Impaired physical mobility related to muscle rigidity and weakness

44. Which one of the following nursing actions is most important to ensure a safe environment for Mrs. Smith?

    1. Assist Mrs. Smith onto the bedpan.
    2. Put one bedside rail up during the day.
    3. Check that Mrs. Smith is in an upright position during mealtimes.
    4. Ask Mrs. Smith to remain in her room during busy times on the unit.

45. Which one of the following diets would best assist Mrs. Smith to meet her nutritional requirements?

    1. A liquid diet
    2. A diet based on her favorite foods
    3. A semisolid diet
    4. A low-carbohydrate diet

46. Which one of the following manifestations should indicate to the nurse that Mrs. Smith is responding well to treatment with levodopa/carbidopa (Sinemet)?
    1. Improvement in dyskinesias
    2. Decreased symptoms of depression
    3. Improvement in bradykinesia and rigidity
    4. Decreased hallucinations and sleep disturbances

47. Which sources of information would be most appropriate for the nurse to consult in the ongoing assessment of Mrs. Smith's ability to carry out her activities of daily living?
    1. The dietitian and pharmacist
    2. The nurses' notes and the physician
    3. The physical and occupational therapists
    4. The social worker and the speech therapist

END OF CASE 19

CASE 20

Judy Summers, a 15-year-old single primigravida, has been admitted to the maternity unit to give birth.

ITEMS 48 to 52 refer to this case.

48. The nurse is discussing Judy's plan of care with a group of nursing students at the bedside. How should the nurse best maintain client privacy?
    1. Speak in a quiet tone of voice.
    2. Ask the students not to discuss Judy's care with her.
    3. Ask the students how Judy's privacy can be maintained.
    4. Pull the curtain around Judy's bed when interviewing her.

49. Judy is in the transitional phase of labor and her mother is with her. Which one of the following needs represents Judy's priority at this time?
    1. Rest
    2. Pain control
    3. Social support
    4. Bowel elimination

50. As labor progresses, Judy becomes anxious and restless. Her membranes rupture as evidenced by meconium staining, and the fetus is in a vertex presentation. Which one of the following actions should the nurse carry out first?

    1. Offer Judy a bedpan.
    2. Provide sedation for Judy.
    3. Assess the fetal heart rate.
    4. Determine the position of the fetus in the uterus.

51. In the postpartum period, which one of the following activities would best promote perineal hygiene?

    1. Shower daily
    2. Tub bath b.i.d.
    3. Sitz bath q.i.d.
    4. Bed bath every morning

52. Judy's care has been assigned to a student nurse. It is the end of the shift and the staff nurse responsible for Judy's care needs to verify that Judy has received teaching regarding breast feeding. When the staff nurse does rounds, Judy is not in her room and the nursing student has left for the day. Which one of the following actions should the staff nurse take first?

    1. Ask another staff nurse if the teaching was given.
    2. Review the student's nursing notes on the teaching.
    3. Ask the other client who shares Judy's room if the teaching was done.
    4. Ask the nurse coming on duty to ask Judy if she received the teaching.

END OF CASE 20

INDEPENDENT ITEMS

ITEMS 53 TO 100 do not refer to a case.

53. A 30-year-old male client who is to be admitted for day surgery is waiting with his wife. What is the most professional way for the nurse to begin a health history interview?

    1. Introduce self and explain the nursing role.
    2. Check the client's wrist identification band.
    3. Invite the client's wife to join the interview.
    4. Ask the client to change into a hospital gown.

54. A 62-year-old client returned from surgery 2 hours ago. Immediately following the administration of a narcotic analgesic by intramuscular injection, which one of the following actions should the nurse take?
    1. Stay with the client to assess the effectiveness of the analgesic.
    2. Assess that this medication is appropriate for the client's pain level.
    3. Document time, dosage, and route of administration of the analgesic.
    4. Verbally report the drug administration prior to leaving for lunch break.

55. When admitting a 10-year-old to the unit, the nurse notices red, raised circular skin patches on the child's right arm. To obtain immediate information about this observation, what source of data should the nurse use?
    1. The child
    2. A reference book
    3. The child's mother
    4. The child's physician

56. Nurse Willis, who is active in a pro-life organization, is asked by the nursing supervisor to care for a client who has undergone a therapeutic abortion. What response by Nurse Willis would indicate practice within the code of ethics?
    1. "I do not wish to care for that client because I do not believe in abortion."
    2. "On this unit, Nurse Bayne cares for the clients who have undergone that procedure."
    3. "That request is outside my area of expertise, please find another nurse to provide the care."
    4. "I would rather not participate in this client's care; could I change assignments with another nurse?"

57. Mrs. Carson, 70 years old, is recovering from day surgery. She has been tolerating oral fluids. At 16 00 hours, the nurse goes into Mrs. Carson's room to discontinue her I.V. and observes her vomiting. Which one of the following interventions is the most appropriate initial action for the nurse to take?
    1. Administer an antiemetic and discontinue the I.V.
    2. Maintain the I.V. infusion and prepare for possible admission.
    3. Continue with discharge plans and make a home care referral.
    4. Notify Mrs. Carson's family that there have been complications.

58. What should the nurse use to prepare an oral liquid medication for administration to a 6-month-old infant?
    1. A plastic teaspoon
    2. A disposable syringe
    3. A disposable dropper
    4. A plastic medication cup

59. Kelly, a 19-year-old construction worker, has been admitted to hospital following a diagnosis of diabetes mellitus. At a health care team meeting, it is determined that Kelly is ready to begin education on self-care. Which one of the following behaviors would indicate Kelly's readiness to learn?

    1. Eating all the food provided on the tray.
    2. Stating that a return to work will be impossible.
    3. Telling the nurse about a friend from work who has diabetes.
    4. Questioning the nurse about why insulin is given in different sites.

60. When the nurse goes into Jay's room, the air smells of marijuana and Jay appears to be euphoric. Which one of the following actions is appropriate for the nurse to take to share this information with the health team?

    1. Call Jay's family for further information.
    2. File a written report with the security department.
    3. Report the incident immediately to Jay's physician.
    4. Document on the care plan that staff should observe for illicit drug use.

61. Mr. Singh is an 84-year-old client receiving furosemide (Lasix) intravenously. Which one of the following actions should the nurse take to monitor for side effects of this medication?

    1. Check for manifestations of hyperkalemia.
    2. Send daily specimens for urine specific gravity.
    3. Observe the client closely for excessive weight gain.
    4. Ask the client if he has had any episodes of dizziness or lightheadedness.

62. Which one of the following sequences of activities by the nurse best describes the steps in the planning phase of the nursing process?

    1. Collect data, identify problems, set goals, prioritize care, evaluate care
    2. Assess the client, identify problems, set goals, and formulate nursing diagnosis
    3. Establish client-centred goals, set time frames to achieve goals, plan interventions, prioritize nursing actions
    4. Collect and analyze data, form nursing diagnosis, conduct appropriate interventions, and evaluate care

63. Mrs. Holmes, age 65, is to be discharged today, 1 week after a total knee replacement. The nurse is concerned that there has been no discussion with Mrs. Holmes, her family, or a community health nurse regarding care at home. Which of the following actions by the nurse is most appropriate?

    1. Give Mrs. Holmes' phone number to the community health nurse.
    2. Provide the required teaching to Mrs. Holmes and her family before she leaves the hospital.
    3. Consult with the health care team to delay discharge until a discharge plan is implemented.
    4. Inform the family, when they arrive, to call Mrs. Holmes' physician with any questions they may have.

64. Kim Jones, age 33, is admitted for the labor induction of her first baby. The induction is to be by oxytocin (Syntocinon), and Kim will have electronic fetal monitoring throughout the process. What would be the most appropriate nursing response when Kim asks the nurse, "Why must I be monitored the whole time?"

    1. "Don't worry, the fetal monitor will not harm you or your baby."
    2. "It is hospital policy that all clients are to be electronically monitored during inductions."
    3. "The monitor is a method for us to see how your baby copes with the stress of labor contractions."
    4. "The fetal monitor will give us enough warning to do a Caesarean section if the baby gets into trouble."

65. Mrs. Dubovsky is a 66-year-old client with mild Alzheimer disease. During the initial assessment, the nurse notes that Mrs. Dubovsky is hesitant to volunteer information. Which one of the following actions should the nurse take to modify the assessment phase?

    1. Collect objective data from the client's family.
    2. Ask simple questions requiring yes-or-no answers.
    3. Realize that Mrs. Dubovsky is generally uncooperative.
    4. Contact the client's physician to provide additional information.

66. While caring for a client, Nurse Jones notices another nurse giving a baby his dose of digoxin (Lanoxin) without taking the baby's apical pulse. Nurse Jones is aware that the other nurse has been reprimanded by the nursing supervisor about unsafe practice. What is the most appropriate action for Nurse Jones to take?

    1. Report the incident to the physician.
    2. Report the incident to the nursing supervisor.
    3. Talk to the other nurse privately about what was observed.
    4. Take the baby's pulse after the other nurse leaves the room.

67. Mrs. Evans, age 62, is being admitted for surgery. During the preoperative interview, the client begins to cry and discuss her husband who died 6 months ago. Which one of the following responses by the nurse would be most effective in demonstrating a helping attitude?

    1. Refer Mrs. Evans to the hospital's bereavement counselor.
    2. Inform Mrs. Evans' daughter that her mother is still grieving.
    3. Acknowledge Mrs. Evans' loss and encourage her to talk about life with her husband.
    4. Introduce Mrs. Evans to another client in the unit who has recently lost her husband and who is coping well.

68. Which one of the following nursing interventions is most important in maintaining peripheral I.V. fluid therapy in an elderly client with altered fluid needs?

    1. Monitor intake and output.
    2. Assess the insertion site for infiltration.
    3. Label the I.V. bag when medications are added.
    4. Administer no more than 100 mL of fluid per hour.

69. Jenny is admitted with neutropenia after a course of chemotherapy. Which one of the following actions indicates that the nurse understands the basic plan of care for this client?

    1. Wear a gown and gloves while providing Jenny's care.
    2. Give Jenny a soft-sponged toothbrush for her mouth care.
    3. Encourage her to use an antiseptic mouthwash after eating.
    4. Ensure that the "No Venipuncture" sign is posted at her bedside.

70. Which one of the following behaviors indicates that the nurse has practiced within the guidelines of the nursing profession?

    1. Using standards of practice to guide nursing care
    2. Comparing performance to that of an expert colleague
    3. Receiving a letter of commendation from a client's family
    4. Delegating administrative nursing functions to the unit clerk

71. Mrs. Cross, age 64, is admitted for investigation of blood in her stool. She has been receiving metoprolol (Lopressor) for 10 months. Her baseline BP is 160/90 mmHg and her pulse is 70 beats/min. Later, before administering the medication, the nurse notes that her BP (lying) is 126/64 mmHg and her pulse is 72 beats/min. What action should the nurse take?

    1. Collect further assessment data.
    2. Check her standing blood pressure.
    3. Withhold the medication temporarily.
    4. Report her vital signs to the physician.

72. Rita, a 16-year-old, is hospitalized for asthma. Which one of the following actions should the nurse take to facilitate Rita's participation in her discharge planning?

    1. Use touch in a therapeutic manner when speaking with Rita.
    2. Make arrangements to interview Rita in the unit conference room.
    3. Request that Rita's mother be present for the discharge planning session.
    4. Ask Rita who she would like to have present during the discharge planning session.

73. How should the nurse justify administering an I.V. of bolus morphine sulfate (Morphine) ordered p.r.n. for a client with terminal cancer who is receiving a continuous morphine infusion?

    1. Anxiety increases the pain threshold.
    2. Clients with cancer can experience breakthrough pain.
    3. The client is addicted to the drug and increased doses are needed.
    4. In terminal cancer, it does not matter how often the client receives the drug.

74. What should be the nurse's first step in demonstrating the use of new nursing knowledge regarding the care of adolescents with eating disorders?

    1. Inform clients that this new knowledge will be incorporated into their plan of care.
    2. Refrain from implementing this new knowledge until receiving direction from the physician.
    3. Accept the professional responsibility of incorporating this new knowledge into the client's plan of care.
    4. Offer to conduct an education session for the health care team, followed by a discussion on how the new knowledge can be implemented.

75. Jordan, age 6, is being discharged in a hip spica cast extending down one leg. Which one of the following adaptations must be made to meet his needs when he returns home?

    1. His parents will have to rent a hospital bed.
    2. His mother will need to buy him loose fitting clothes.
    3. Arrangements will have to be made to rent a wheelchair.
    4. A home care worker will be required to assist with turning him.

76. Which one of the following statements by the nurse would help establish a professional relationship with Mr. Murray Fox, 70 years old, upon admission to the hospital?

    1. "Hello, Mr. Fox. I'm Robin Grey, your nurse. I will be here to answer any of your questions."
    2. "Good day, Mr. Fox. My name is Robin. Your doctor will be in to see you after you are settled."
    3. "Good afternoon Murray. I'm Robin Grey. I will be your primary nurse while you are in the hospital."
    4. "Hi, Murray. This is Pat, your roommate, and I'm Robin. I'll be back to ask you some questions once you are in bed."

77. Ms. Pickell is a 64-year-old client who has a 3-week-old colostomy stoma. For the past week, she has been managing her care at home. During a home visit, the nurse notes that the skin around the stoma has become reddened and tender. Which one of the following actions by the nurse is most appropriate?

    1. Ask Ms. Pickell what she thinks she may be doing incorrectly.
    2. Have Ms. Pickell change her colostomy pouch and assist as necessary.
    3. Change the colostomy pouch for Ms. Pickell using a skin barrier/paste to protect the skin around the stoma.
    4. Change the colostomy pouch for Ms. Pickell, cleansing gently with warm water and drying the skin thoroughly.

78. Two hours postoperatively, 64-year-old Mr. Davis exhibits the following manifestations: restlessness; pulse pressure has dropped 20 mmHg; pulse rate has increased to 100 beats/min. Which one of the following actions is the most appropriate nursing response to this situation?

    1. Document the assessment data.
    2. Consult the physician immediately.
    3. Place the client in Sims' position.
    4. Reassess the client's condition every half hour.

79. A nurse from the intensive care unit (ICU) is assigned to help on one of the medical units. On arrival to the unit, the nurse is assigned 5 clients and realizes that the workload is extremely heavy. Which one of the following actions should the nurse take to ensure that the care requirements of all 5 clients will be met?

    1. Provide as much care as possible and then enlist assistance from the next shift.
    2. Inform the nursing supervisor that the usual workload in the ICU consists of 2 clients per shift.
    3. Prioritize the care needs of the clients, and give each client's family members a plan of care to follow.
    4. Consult the nursing supervisor about the heavy workload and delegate the non-nursing care functions to the health care aide.

80. The nurse approaches Mrs. Chisolm before her hysterectomy to teach her about hormone replacement therapy. Mrs. Chisolm tells the nurse that she does not believe in hormone therapy. In modifying the plan of care to further assess the client's knowledge of the medication, what is the expected outcome?

    1. The nurse discusses the problem with the multidisciplinary team.
    2. The physician cancels the order for hormone replacement therapy.
    3. The client agrees to take the hormone replacement therapy as ordered.
    4. The client discusses the advantages and disadvantages of hormone replacement therapy.

81. Mr. Johnson is a 63-year-old man who lives alone. He is taking a diuretic at supper time, but says his sleep is disturbed because of frequent trips to the bathroom at night. Which one of the following interventions would be appropriate for the nurse to suggest to Mr. Johnson?

    1. "Try to rest throughout the day."
    2. "Get up slowly from your bed if you feel dizzy."
    3. "Take the medication early in the day so your sleep won't be disturbed."
    4. "Reduce the amount of medicine you are taking, and inform your doctor."

82. Mrs. Chadwell is admitted to hospital with a diagnosis of malignant hypertension. Two hours following treatment, she complains of a headache and blurred vision, and her blood pressure remains unchanged. The nurse consults the physician by phone but the physician cannot see the client for 4 hours. Which one of the following responses by the nurse is most appropriate?

    1. "I will monitor her vital signs closely until you arrive."
    2. "Can you come sooner or do I have to call someone in authority?"
    3. "This client needs to be seen by a physician now. Who should I call?"
    4. "This client requires additional medication. What would you like to order?"

83. Which one of the following interventions will best prevent infections in a pediatric burn unit?

    1. Assign each client to a private room.
    2. Practice wound and skin precautions.
    3. Send swabs of the clients' burns for culture and sensitivity tests.
    4. Have client families provide all play materials for their children.

84. A client is admitted to hospital for treatment of acute peritonitis. In assessing the client's abdomen, which of the following physical assessment techniques should the nurse use?

    1. Inspection; palpation
    2. Palpation; percussion
    3. Inspection; auscultation
    4. Auscultation; percussion

85. Mr. Grey, 75 years old, suffered a myocardial infarction (MI) 4 days ago. When developing his care plan, what activity should the nurse encourage him to do on his fifth day post-MI?

    1. Move around freely in his room.
    2. Perform isometric exercises q.i.d.
    3. Climb a flight of stairs once daily.
    4. Ambulate the full length of the hospital corridor.

86. The nurse has developed a teaching plan for a client. Which one of the following actions by the nurse would best ensure that the teaching plan is communicated to the other members of the health care team?

    1. Inform the senior nurses and request that they inform the other members of the team.

    2. Discuss the teaching plan on a one-to-one basis with other members of the health care team.

    3. Arrange a meeting of the health care workers involved with the client to discuss the teaching plan.

    4. Place a note on the front of the client's chart indicating that a teaching plan has been developed for the client.

87. Jane, age 15, tells the nurse that she is considering having sexual relations and would like some information on effective birth control methods. Which one of the following responses by the nurse would indicate acceptance of Jane's sexuality?

    1. "You will need to see your family doctor for this information."

    2. "Don't you think it's early to be thinking about having sexual relations?"

    3. "Do your parents know that you are considering having sexual relations?"

    4. "Let's sit down and talk more about your need for birth control information."

88. Fifteen-year-old Pat has been admitted to the intensive care unit (ICU) with multiple trauma. ICU policy states that no children under 12 are allowed to visit. Pat requests that his 10-year-old brother be allowed to visit. What action should the nurse take in response to Pat's request?

    1. Report Pat's concerns to the physician to facilitate follow-up.

    2. Tell Pat that his brother can visit in the evening when the unit is not as busy.

    3. Consult the hospital social worker to assist Pat in dealing with his loneliness.

    4. Discuss Pat's concerns with the nursing supervisor and determine how an exception can be made in the ICU policy.

89. Mr. Brown, age 70, has become increasingly dyspneic. What should the nurse do to promote ventilation and make him more comfortable?

    1. Take his vital signs.

    2. Encourage him to ambulate.

    3. Assist him to a supine position.

    4. Administer oxygen 2 L/min as ordered.

90. Mr. Redmond, age 67, has complications from bowel surgery. He was placed on total parenteral nutrition through a central venous line six days ago. The client begins to exhibit symptoms of anxiety, chest pain, and "a feeling of doom." Which one of the following actions is most appropriate for the nurse to take?

    1. Lay him on his left side.
    2. Ask him to breathe deeply.
    3. Slow down the rate of his infusion.
    4. Assist him to a high-Fowler's position.

91. How should the nurse assist a slightly confused, elderly male to dress?

    1. Instruct him on how to put on his clothes.
    2. Help him to dress in clothes selected by the nurse.
    3. Anticipate his needs by selecting his clothes for him.
    4. Allow him to choose between two articles of clothing.

92. Which one of the following actions best demonstrates a nurse's ability for self-assessment as a care provider?

    1. Assessing clients' progress
    2. Requesting a peer review of performance
    3. Seeking help upon recognizing limitations
    4. Asking clients for their perceptions of the care provided

93. Three-year-old Johanna is admitted at 23 00 hours with acute asthma. Ventolin masks are prescribed q. 3h overnight. At 05 00 hours, the child's respirations are 24 breaths/min and easy, pulse is 96 beats/min, retractions are absent, and fine expiratory wheezes are audible per stethoscope. Which one of the following interventions by the nurse is most appropriate?

    1. Gently awaken the child and administer the next prescribed mask.
    2. Continue to monitor the child's respiratory status q. 30 minutes while she sleeps.
    3. Allow the child to sleep for an additional hour, then return to administer the mask.
    4. Skip one medication administration due to an observed improvement in the child's respiratory status.

94. Which one of the following nursing actions would best assist the family of a 65-year-old man who has just died?

    1. Leave the family alone with the deceased.
    2. Ask the family to assist in bathing the body.
    3. Remain with the family while they view the body.
    4. Give the family permission to see the body briefly.

95. The arterial blood gas report for a 60-year-old client indicates:

  - pH: 7.29
  - PaCO$_2$: 60 mmHg
  - HCO$_3$:   24 mEq/L

  The nurse should recognize that the client is exhibiting which one of the following conditions?

  1. Metabolic acidosis
  2. Metabolic alkalosis
  3. Respiratory acidosis
  4. Respiratory alkalosis

96. The clinic nurse teaches Mr. Baxter, age 65, about the importance of a low-cholesterol diet in reducing his risk of heart disease. Which one of the following statements by Mr. Baxter would indicate that he understands the teaching?

  1. "I will clear any blocked blood vessels by eating more cheese."
  2. "My heart will become stronger when I increase my daily intake of calcium."
  3. "By decreasing the red meat in my diet, I will reduce my chance of heart disease."
  4. "By having peanut butter on my toast every morning, I will lower my cholesterol."

97. Sixty-year-old Mrs. Jessome has cancer, and nasogastric feedings are ordered. After Mrs. Jessome pulls out the nasogastric tube twice, wrist restraints are ordered. As a client advocate, which of the following actions should the nurse take?

  1. Explore with Mrs. Jessome why she continues to pull out the tube.
  2. Give Mrs. Jessome a sedative to increase her cooperation during feedings.
  3. Explain to Mrs. Jessome why the restraints are required and gently place them on her wrists.
  4. Suggest that a staff person sit with Mrs. Jessome while the feedings are being administered.

98. Which one of the following actions is most appropriate for the nurse to take when caring for an 80-year-old client following surgery?

  1. Pace the nursing care activities based on the client's needs.
  2. Allow the client to determine what care is desired and at what time.
  3. Permit the client to sleep, and delay some nursing activities until later in the shift.
  4. Complete all pertinent care and therapies at one time, then allow the client to rest.

99. Mrs. Ostrowski, a 75-year-old widow with limited resources, is discussing nutritional needs with the home care nurse. She lives in a large city, several blocks from the store, does not drive, and finds it difficult to cook for herself. Which one of the following suggestions should the nurse make to Mrs. Ostrowski?

1. Visit the city's food bank.
2. Have a neighbor drive her to the store.
3. Buy food in bulk when she goes shopping.
4. Use the Meals-on-Wheels program.

100. Which one of the following nursing entries would represent concise and organized charting?

1. 08 00-Client watching TV while sitting in bed. Bath given. Dressing changed, up in chair.
2. 08 00-Client sitting in bed and states he is feeling good. Total bath given with no problems. Dressing changed, incision looks good. Up to chair without much help.
3. 08 00-Client sitting in bed watching TV. Total bath given, tolerated without signs of fatigue. Dressing to left leg changed: no drainage on old dressing, incision line well approximated with no redness or swelling. Moved to chair with minimal assistance.
4. 08 00-Client sitting in semi-Fowler's position in his bed. He has the TV on and states, "This is my favorite program." Total bed bath given, Mr. Jones was able to help me a little. Dressing then changed, his old dressing had no drainage and his incision line showed no signs of infection as there was no redness or swelling. I then moved him to the chair by holding his arm when he moved.

END OF INDEPENDENT ITEMS

CASE 21

Arthur Clements is a 52-year-old man who is obese and hypertensive. He is hospitalized with a recent diagnosis of non-insulin-dependent (Type II) diabetes mellitus.

ITEMS 101 to 105 refer to this case.

101. Which one of the following instructions should the nurse include in teaching Mr. Clements to record his usual intake?

1. Ask him to record his intake according to the basic food groups.
2. Ask him to record his daily physical activities along with his food intake.
3. Instruct him to follow a 7-day meal plan and to record all items consumed.
4. Instruct him to confine his record keeping to foods consumed at mealtimes.

102. Mr. Clements is off the unit for 1 hour at a diabetic teaching session when his daily dose of antihypertensive medication is due. Which of the following actions should the nurse take?
    1. Call the classroom and have Mr. Clements' return for his medication.
    2. Give the medication upon Mr. Clements' return to the unit and record it as given at the scheduled time.
    3. Arrange to have medication taken to Mr. Clements and record it in the chart as given.
    4. Give the medication on Mr. Clements' return and note in the chart the reason for the late administration.

103. The nurse observes that Mr. Clements' feet are dry and callused and that his toenails are thick. He states that he has cold feet. Which one of the following actions should the nurse take to promote healthy feet?
    1. Consult a foot care specialist.
    2. Expose his feet to air at all times.
    3. Inspect his feet for injury q. 1 week.
    4. Apply a heating pad to his lower legs.

104. Which one of the following activities is associated with the nurse's role in evaluating Mr. Clements' nursing care?
    1. Ensuring that all the nursing goals have been met
    2. Identifying factors that interfered with the achievement of nursing care goals
    3. Identifying objective evidence that Mr. Clements' diabetes is responding to treatment
    4. Referring unresolved nursing diagnoses to Mr. Clements' family on his discharge from the hospital

105. While drawing blood from Mr. Clements, the nurse sustains a needle-stick injury to the finger. The injury is sufficient to cause bleeding. How should the nurse manage the needle-stick injury?
    1. Apply pressure to the injury to stop the bleeding.
    2. Arrange for an immediate blood test to determine if the nurse has contracted HIV.
    3. Bandage the injured part securely to protect it from further injury and contamination.
    4. Arrange for vaccination for the hepatitis B virus if the nurse was not previously immunized.

END OF CASE 21

CASE 22

Mrs. Perry is a 70-year-old woman who has been admitted to hospital because she has developed signs of acute renal failure. She is in the oliguric phase, and complains of nausea and drowsiness.

ITEMS 106 to 111 refer to this case.

106. The specific gravity of Mrs. Perry's urine is low. Lab data reveal hyponatremia and hyperkalemia. What further assessment of Mrs. Perry should the nurse conduct?
    1. Listen to her chest.
    2. Note signs of hypovolemia.
    3. Observe for postural hypotension.
    4. Assess signs of fluid volume deficit.

107. Which one of the following nursing actions should be a priority in planning care for Mrs. Perry?
    1. Encourage oral fluid intake.
    2. Weigh the client before meals.
    3. Leave the side rails up at all times.
    4. Encourage independence in activities of daily living.

108. Which one of the following nursing interventions should be a priority for the nurse to perform with Mrs. Perry hourly?
    1. Turn and position.
    2. Measure urinary output.
    3. Promote deep breathing.
    4. Check for signs of edema.

109. The nurse answers Mrs. Perry's call light to find her looking very agitated and holding a kidney basin that is full of blood. She exclaims, "Nurse, look what's happened! Am I bleeding to death?" Which one of the following responses by the nurse would be most appropriate?
    1. "Wait right there and I'll get the doctor at the desk."
    2. "What were you doing that could have caused this?"
    3. "It can be pretty scary when you're bleeding. Let me help you."
    4. "No, you're not bleeding to death. It always looks worse than it is."

GO TO NEXT PAGE

110.   A float nurse, unfamiliar with the unit, is assigned to care for Mrs. Perry. What should the charge nurse do to ensure that any noticeable changes in Mrs. Perry's condition are reported?

1.   Check the float nurse's charting.
2.   Verify the float nurse's assessment.
3.   Review with the float nurse what should be assessed and reported.
4.   Ask the nurse working in the next room to be available to the float nurse.

111.   Mrs. Perry has been making satisfactory progress and her I.V. has been discontinued. What intervention should the nurse take to ensure that Mrs. Perry's food and fluid needs will continue to be met?

1.   Provide milkshakes t.i.d.
2.   Ensure her privacy during meals.
3.   Encourage a high-calorie breakfast.
4.   Measure her intake and output, and give her water between meals.

END OF CASE 22

CASE 23

Paul Fee is an 18-year-old college student. He has a complete spinal cord lesion at T1 and a closed-head injury as a result of a diving accident which happened 1 week ago. He has remained unconscious since his admission.

ITEMS 112 to 117 refer to this case.

112.   The nurse and Paul's mother are bathing him. Which one of the following approaches by the nurse would best promote a helping relationship between the nurse, Paul, and Paul's mother?

1.   Address Paul, saying, "Paul, your mom is here helping to wash you."
2.   Quietly say to Paul's mother, "You must be worried about Paul's recovery."
3.   Speak slowly and clearly to Paul, saying, "Please just try to open your eyes for your mom."
4.   Reduce auditory stimulation and whisper to Paul's mother, "Why don't you give him a back rub?"

113. Paul has been started on total parenteral nutrition (TPN). During a bag change, the bag containing the solution of amino acids is inadvertently punctured by the spike on the tubing. Which one of the following interventions by the nurse would best maintain the TPN infusion?

    1. Tape the hole with sterile, waterproof tape and continue the infusion.
    2. Slow the infusion and wait for a new bag to be delivered from the pharmacy.
    3. Continue the infusion with Dextrose 10% until a new bag is available from the pharmacy.
    4. Increase the rate of the lipid infusion until a new bag of amino acids can be administered.

114. Which one of the following nursing actions would be most effective in promoting circulation in Paul's lower limbs?

    1. Apply resting splints to both legs.
    2. Flex and extend the client's ankles q. 2h.
    3. Administer warm packs to both calves t.i.d.
    4. Elevate the foot of the client's bed 15 cm with a slight knee bend.

115. In managing the physical environment, which one of the following measures should the nurse perform to promote safety for Paul?

    1. Keep the lights in Paul's room dimmed.
    2. Ensure the bed sheets are free of wrinkles.
    3. Turn Paul from prone to supine positions q. 2h.
    4. Have the curtains around Paul's bed open at all times.

116. During the night shift, the nurse caring for Paul and three other spinal cord injured clients becomes involved in the care of an unstable client and cannot attend to the other clients. What should the nurse do to ensure a safe practice environment?

    1. Document the situation, and provide a rationale for the decisions made.
    2. Advise the nursing supervisor of the situation and request assistance on the unit.
    3. Leave the unstable client in a recovery position and proceed to perform care for the other clients.
    4. Ask the practical nurse/nursing assistant to stay with the unstable client while the nurse attends to the other clients.

117. The nurse frequently dreams about being paralyzed and questions the ethical implications of the care provided for Paul, wondering, "Wouldn't he be better off dead?" Which one of the following actions by the nurse would best promote personal and professional growth?

    1. Request immediate use of accumulated vacation time.
    2. Apply for a transfer to a less demanding unit.
    3. Approach colleagues to see how they have dealt with similar experiences.
    4. Recognize that these feelings are a normal part of professional growth and that they will be resolved in time.

END OF CASE 23

INDEPENDENT ITEMS

ITEMS 118 to 129 do <u>not</u> refer to a case.

118. Mabel O'Brian, 75 years old, is experiencing severe rheumatoid arthritic symptoms. She reluctantly uses prescribed medications, relying mostly on home remedies. The nurse identifies that Mabel has a knowledge deficit regarding self-management of her health situation. How should the nurse validate this with the client?

    1. Ask her if the pills upset her stomach.
    2. Inquire about the home remedies she uses.
    3. Explore the client's need for home care follow-up.
    4. Assess the client's understanding of her medications.

119. During the nurse's performance appraisal interview, the nursing supervisor tells the nurse that treatments are carried out in an organized manner and that the nurse is a good team member. However, the nursing supervisor concludes the interview by criticizing the nurse's charting. Which one of the following responses by the nurse would best indicate a receptiveness to change?

    1. "My own assessment of my charting is that I am clear and concise."
    2. "You just told me I was a good team member. I am not sure I understand what you mean."
    3. "I appreciate you taking the time to give me feedback about my clinical performance."
    4. "Thank you for the feedback. Do you have any suggestions to help me improve my charting?"

120. Which one of the following actions should the nurse take when using a stretcher to move a client with an indwelling catheter?

    1. Connect the catheter to a leg drainage bag.
    2. Hang the drainage bag over the end of the stretcher.
    3. Attach the drainage bag to the siderail of the stretcher.
    4. Put the tube and drainage bag between the client's legs.

121. The nurse observes a nursing colleague using an unsafe practice when initiating I.V. therapy. Which one of the following actions by the nurse is most appropriate as a client advocate?

    1. Inform the client that his safety is at risk.
    2. Report the problem to the Director of Nursing.
    3. Discuss the situation with the colleague immediately.
    4. Request that the colleague assist the nurse the next time I.V. therapy is initiated.

122. Which one of the following responses by the nurse best demonstrates a therapeutic communication technique with a 65-year-old man who is very concerned about a bad cold he has had for more than a week?

    1. "Did you have your flu shot this year?"
    2. "This sure is the time of year for colds. Everyone has one!"
    3. "You're afraid that your cold might develop into pneumonia."
    4. "You're upset that you have had a cold for more than a week."

123. Jamie is a 10-year-old boy who received a deep laceration to his scalp when he fell off a play structure. The nurse assesses that Jamie's injury will require suturing by the physician. Which one of the following interventions should be taken by the nurse to promote tissue integrity?

    1. Allow the laceration to remain open to the air until the suturing can be completed.
    2. After cleansing the injury, apply a sterile dressing until the suturing can be completed.
    3. Observe the site for 24 hours to assess the extent of injury before preparation for suturing.
    4. Leave the original pressure dressing in place for at least 3 hours to prevent hemorrhage.

124. A 17-year-old female client who has been diagnosed with herpes genitalis says to the nurse, "Be honest with me. What can happen to me now that I have herpes?" Which one of the following responses by the nurse is most appropriate?

    1. "Once these sores are healed, you should expect episodes about five times a year."
    2. "There are no long-term effects of herpes once the sores are healed; you can even become pregnant some day."
    3. "You will require special care when you are pregnant and there is a higher incidence of cervical cancer with herpes."
    4. "We'll discuss the long-term effects next week when you come for further counseling. I don't want to overwhelm you today."

125. Mary Anne is a 15-year-old client diagnosed with anorexia nervosa. She is currently in a behavior modification program. Which one of the following outcomes would indicate that Mary Anne's family understands the principles of behavior modification?

    1. They bring in Mary Anne's favorite snacking foods to encourage her to eat.
    2. They plan to have a party for Mary Anne to celebrate her upcoming birthday.
    3. They accept the nursing staff's decision to withdraw visiting privileges when Mary Anne fails to gain weight.
    4. Because they want to show their support for Mary Anne, they indicate that negative reinforcement should come only from the nurses.

126. Which one of the following actions by the nurse best illustrates the application of surgical asepsis when dressing a client's abdominal incision?

    1. Hold wet forceps with the tips down.
    2. Cleanse the incision from bottom to top.
    3. Wear sterile gloves and mask for dressing changes.
    4. Place the sterile supplies near the edge of the sterile field for easier access.

127. A 14-year-old female client has just been diagnosed with insulin-dependent (Type I) diabetes mellitus. She asks the nurse, "How is my life going to change because of my diabetes?" Which one of the following responses by the nurse is most appropriate?

    1. "Diabetes will not change your life."
    2. "You will need to follow a strict diet."
    3. "You will need to develop interests other than sports."
    4. "You will have to learn some new skills to manage your diabetes."

128. Rita is a 23-year-old homeless woman who has just been diagnosed with schizophrenia. Her behavior since admission has been unpredictable. Which one of the following nursing interventions is likely to be most effective in promoting a safe environment for this client?

    1. Provide Rita with a private room.
    2. Confront Rita about her behavior.
    3. Ensure frequent observation of Rita.
    4. Initiate a structured social activity for Rita.

129. Michael is an 18-year-old who is admitted to the psychiatric unit with a diagnosis of bipolar disorder. He is started on lithium carbonate (Lithizine) 300 mg t.i.d. During visiting hours, the nurse notices that he sings and tells jokes, disturbing the staff and other clients. Which one of the following measures should the nurse implement to modify the situation?

    1. Provide feedback to him about his behavior.
    2. Reduce environmental stimuli by moving him to a quiet place.
    3. Closely supervise him to ensure that he takes his lithium carbonate.
    4. Promote his self-esteem by listening to his singing and joke telling.

END OF INDEPENDENT ITEMS

END OF EXAMINATION

CHAPTER

5

Scoring the Practice Exam

SCORING THE PRACTICE EXAM

CALCULATING YOUR SCORE

The following steps can be used to calculate your **total raw score** on the Practice Exam.

1. Locate the answer keys for the Practice Exam (see pages 110 and 111). Note that there is one key per exam book.

2. Tally up your responses that correspond to the correct answers indicated on the answer key. (Identify those questions you answered incorrectly by circling or highlighting them on your response sheet, or by listing them on a separate sheet of paper. This will make it easier for you to create your Performance Profile, an exercise which is explained in the next chapter.)

3. Score **one** point for each correct answer. There is no penalty for incorrect or blank responses; they receive a score of zero. Be sure to scan your response sheet for "double responses" to questions (i.e., where you selected more than one answer to a single question). Double responses are scored as zero, even if one of the answers selected is correct.

4. Use the chart below to record your score on each exam book and to calculate your total raw score.

NUMBER OF QUESTIONS ANSWERED CORRECTLY	
BOOK 1	_____/129
BOOK 2	_____/129
TOTAL RAW SCORE	_____/258
(sum of Books 1 + 2)	

5. Once you have added together your scores for each book in the Practice Exam, you will have your total raw score. The next calculation you can make is to convert your total raw score into a percentage score. This may be done using the following formula:

PERCENTAGE SCORE

$$\frac{\text{TOTAL RAW SCORE}}{258} \times 100 = \underline{\quad}\%$$

INTERPRETING YOUR SCORE

Although the total raw score and percentage score that you calculate are of a different type than the result you would receive on the actual RN Exam (see next section), they can provide useful feedback on your performance. By using the Score Interpretation Scale on page 109, you can obtain a quick assessment of your performance on the Practice Exam, along with some follow-up steps you should take to enhance your preparation for the RN Exam. Note that no specific pass mark is set for the Practice Exam.

HOW THE ACTUAL RN EXAM IS SCORED

The RN Exam is computer scored by CNAT. Only answers recorded on your response sheets are scanned and scored. You will not receive any credit for questions that you only answered directly in the exam books and not on the response sheets. Likewise, no credit will be given where you selected more than one answer to a single question. It is essential that you read and follow the instructions inside each exam book on how to correctly mark your selected answers; otherwise, your score may be adversely affected.

Once your response sheets for both exam books are scanned, your score on the examination is calculated and your "pass" or "fail" result is determined by comparing this score to the established standard (or pass mark).

The standard to be met on the RN Exam is established, prior to the administration of the examination, using a criterion-referenced approach. Such an approach involves setting the standard in reference to the content and the difficulty of the test items. This is in contrast to the norm-referenced approach, which sets the standard in relation to the performance of the examinees.

The standard-setting procedure used by CNAT involves convening panels of subject matter experts from across Canada to determine a point on a measurement scale that represents the expected performance of a minimally competent nurse beginning to practice. These subject matter experts are nurses who work closely with nurses beginning to practice, and include educators, experienced practitioners, and administrators. Prior to performing their task, the subject matter experts are provided with an extensive orientation and training by CNAT staff, to ensure that they produce ratings based on the same understanding of the minimally competent beginning practitioner.

In addition to the expert ratings, a variety of relevant data is carefully considered to ensure that the standard that examinees will be required to achieve on the exam is valid and fair. This can include information on the preparation of new graduates, data on the performance of examinees on previously administered exams, and pertinent psychometric research findings. Based on all of this information, a point is set on a measurement scale that represents the minimum acceptable standard.

Regardless of the version of the examination that is administered, an examinee's score is converted to a common measurement scale and compared against the established passing point on that scale. Although different forms of the exam contain different sets of questions, this conversion ensures that all examinees are treated fairly and are evaluated against the same standard. If your score on this common scale is at or higher than the passing point, you will receive a "pass" result on the exam and if your score is lower than the passing point you will receive a "fail" result on the exam.

Your pass/fail result on the RN Exam is reported on a Candidate Examination Report that is sent to you by your provincial/territorial registering/licensing authority. Examinees who fail the RN Exam are also provided with feedback on their test performance. This feedback is similar to the information you will obtain by creating your Performance Profile (see Chapter 6).

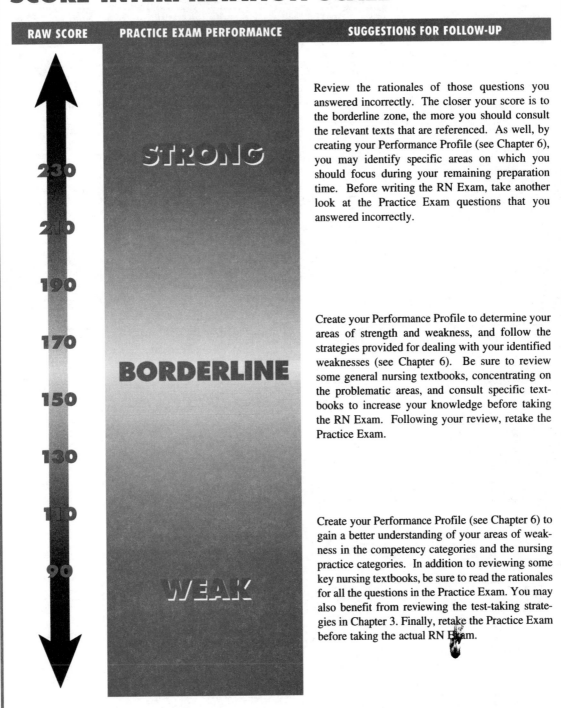

SCORE INTERPRETATION SCALE

RAW SCORE	PRACTICE EXAM PERFORMANCE	SUGGESTIONS FOR FOLLOW-UP

230
210
190

STRONG

Review the rationales of those questions you answered incorrectly. The closer your score is to the borderline zone, the more you should consult the relevant texts that are referenced. As well, by creating your Performance Profile (see Chapter 6), you may identify specific areas on which you should focus during your remaining preparation time. Before writing the RN Exam, take another look at the Practice Exam questions that you answered incorrectly.

170
150
130

BORDERLINE

Create your Performance Profile to determine your areas of strength and weakness, and follow the strategies provided for dealing with your identified weaknesses (see Chapter 6). Be sure to review some general nursing textbooks, concentrating on the problematic areas, and consult specific textbooks to increase your knowledge before taking the RN Exam. Following your review, retake the Practice Exam.

110
90

WEAK

Create your Performance Profile (see Chapter 6) to gain a better understanding of your areas of weakness in the competency categories and the nursing practice categories. In addition to reviewing some key nursing textbooks, be sure to read the rationales for all the questions in the Practice Exam. You may also benefit from reviewing the test-taking strategies in Chapter 3. Finally, retake the Practice Exam before taking the actual RN Exam.

5

ANSWER KEY – BOOK 1

QUESTION NUMBER	CORRECT ANSWER
1.	2
2.	3
3.	1
4.	1
5.	4
6.	2
7.	3
8.	2
9.	3
10.	1
11.	2
12.	3
13.	4
14.	1
15.	4
16.	3
17.	2
18.	3
19.	1
20.	2
21.	1
22.	4
23.	3
24.	3
25.	2
26.	4
27.	3
28.	1
29.	3
30.	3
31.	3
32.	4
33.	3

QUESTION NUMBER	CORRECT ANSWER
34.	3
35.	3
36.	4
37.	4
38.	4
39.	3
40.	4
41.	2
42.	1
43.	1
44.	3
45.	3
46.	1
47.	4
48.	3
49.	2
50.	4
51.	4
52.	3
53.	3
54.	4
55.	4
56.	4
57.	4
58.	1
59.	2
60.	2
61.	2
62.	3
63.	2
64.	2
65.	3
66.	1

QUESTION NUMBER	CORRECT ANSWER
67.	3
68.	3
69.	1
70.	3
71.	4
72.	1
73.	4
74.	4
75.	4
76.	2
77.	2
78.	1
79.	4
80.	3
81.	1
82.	4
83.	3
84.	3
85.	2
86.	3
87.	1
88.	2
89.	2
90.	3
91.	3
92.	4
93.	2
94.	2
95.	3
96.	2
97.	2
98.	3
99.	1

QUESTION NUMBER	CORRECT ANSWER
100.	4
101.	4
102.	1
103.	2
104.	3
105.	2
106.	2
107.	3
108.	2
109.	3
110.	4
111.	3
112.	1
113.	3
114.	4
115.	4
116.	1
117.	2
118.	2
119.	3
120.	1
121.	1
122.	3
123.	3
124.	1
125.	1
126.	1
127.	1
128.	3
129.	2

ANSWER KEY – BOOK 2

QUESTION NUMBER	CORRECT ANSWER
1.	1
2.	3
3.	1
4.	4
5.	2
6.	2
7.	2
8.	1
9.	4
10.	1
11.	3
12.	3
13.	2
14.	1
15.	1
16.	1
17.	4
18.	3
19.	2
20.	3
21.	2
22.	2
23.	3
24.	2
25.	1
26.	1
27.	1
28.	1
29.	1
30.	2
31.	3
32.	4
33.	2

QUESTION NUMBER	CORRECT ANSWER
34.	3
35.	2
36.	1
37.	3
38.	4
39.	3
40.	2
41.	4
42.	1
43.	4
44.	3
45.	3
46.	3
47.	3
48.	4
49.	2
50.	3
51.	3
52.	2
53.	1
54.	3
55.	1
56.	4
57.	2
58.	2
59.	4
60.	4
61.	4
62.	3
63.	3
64.	3
65.	2
66.	2

QUESTION NUMBER	CORRECT ANSWER
67.	3
68.	2
69.	3
70.	1
71.	1
72.	4
73.	2
74.	4
75.	2
76.	1
77.	2
78.	2
79.	4
80.	4
81.	3
82.	3
83.	2
84.	3
85.	1
86.	3
87.	4
88.	4
89.	4
90.	1
91.	4
92.	3
93.	1
94.	3
95.	3
96.	3
97.	1
98.	1
99.	4

QUESTION NUMBER	CORRECT ANSWER
100.	3
101.	2
102.	4
103.	1
104.	2
105.	4
106.	1
107.	3
108.	2
109.	3
110.	3
111.	3
112.	1
113.	3
114.	2
115.	2
116.	2
117.	3
118.	4
119.	4
120.	2
121.	3
122.	4
123.	2
124.	3
125.	3
126.	1
127.	4
128.	3
129.	2

5

CHAPTER

6

Creating your Performance Profile

CREATING YOUR PERFORMANCE PROFILE

Once you have completed and scored the Practice Exam, it is possible to create a personalized Performance Profile that allows you to identify your areas of strength and weakness on the exam, based on the Competency Category and Nursing Practice classifications. You will need your scored response sheets (or a list of the questions you answered incorrectly), the Performance Profile Tally Sheet and Performance Profile Chart (found at the end of the *Prep Guide*), and a calculator.

CLASSIFICATION OF QUESTIONS

Each question in the Practice Exam has been classified within four different classification schemes: Competency Category, Taxonomic Level, Client Age Group, and Nursing Practice. Each question's classifications are indicated beside the question's rationale in Chapter 7.

The first three classification schemes (i.e., Competency Category, Taxonomic Level, and Client Age Group) are weighted elements from the *Blueprint*, and an explanation of these can be found in Chapter 2. The fourth classification, Nursing Practice, is not a weighted element of the *Blueprint*; a description of this classification is provided below. The Competency Categories and Nursing Practice classifications will be used to create your Performance Profile.

NURSING PRACTICE CLASSIFICATION

In the Nursing Practice classification, each item has been classified by the nature of the care nurses provide to their clients. There are eight categories used within this classification. Although there may be overlap in the content that is being assessed by any one question, each question on the Practice Exam has been classified into just one category of Nursing Practice.

The eight categories used for the Nursing Practice classification on the *Prep Guide* Practice Exam are as follows:

1. **Physiological Needs** includes concepts related to providing for basic human needs such as comfort and safety, hygiene, body alignment, exercise and activity, rest, sleep, nutrition, elimination, respiration, fluid and electrolyte balance, circulation, and the regulation of temperature, senses, and endocrine glands.

2. **Psychosocial Needs** includes concepts related to meeting clients' needs associated with self-concept, self-esteem, body image, sexuality, beliefs, spirituality, grief, coping mechanisms, behavior, and maladaptive behavior patterns.

3. **Screening and Diagnosis** includes concepts related to assessing clients, such as data collection, problem identification based on the analysis of clinical data and the establishment of corresponding nursing diagnoses, collection of supplemental data through diagnostic tests, and explaining/interpreting diagnostic procedures.

4. **Clinical Techniques** includes concepts related to providing hands-on or technical care to clients, such as catheterization, wound and stoma care, suctioning, oxygen, relief of pain, cast care, traction devices, application of heat and cold, positioning, etc.

5. **Pharmacology** includes concepts involved with nursing practice related to medications, such as drug preparation and administration, drug actions and side effects, and legal issues connected with drug administration. It also includes concepts related to the client's knowledge of medications; e.g., teaching clients about drug actions, evaluating knowledge of side-effects, promoting cooperation with medication regimens, etc.

6

6. **Communication** includes concepts related to interviewing, therapeutic communication techniques, the helping relationship, and health teaching. Within health teaching, the questions focus on principles of teaching, including the nurse's evaluation of health teaching.

7. **Professional Responsibilities** includes concepts related to professional standards of practice, use of the nursing process, evaluating nursing care, legal, ethical, collaborative, or administrative aspects of nursing as well as communicating with other members of the nursing or health team through health records or interdisciplinary meetings, etc.

8. **General** is a category used for more generic questions that do not specifically fall within one of the other seven areas.

STEPS FOR CREATING YOUR PERFORMANCE PROFILE

1. In scoring your Practice Exam with the information provided in the previous chapter, you identified on your response sheets (or on a separate sheet), those questions you answered incorrectly. For each question answered **incorrectly** place an X beside the corresponding classifications in the rationale section (Chapter 7).

2. The **Performance Profile Tally Sheet** and the **Performance Profile Chart** are located at the back of the *Prep Guide* and can be easily removed for you to use. Each of these contains two tables, Table A and Table B. In Table A of the Tally Sheet, for each question you answered incorrectly, place a mark in the row that corresponds to the Competency category for that question (see Sample – Step 2). Similarly, in Table B, place a mark in the row that corresponds to the Nursing Practice category for each question you answered incorrectly.

SAMPLE — STEP 2

PERFORMANCE PROFILE TALLY SHEET

TABLE A: COMPETENCY CATEGORY

CATEGORY		TOTAL INCORRECT		% INCORRECT
DC ‖‖‖ ‖‖‖		÷ 19 X 100 =		%
AI ‖‖‖		÷ 17 X 100 =		%
PC ‖‖‖ ‖‖‖ ‖		÷ 20 X 100 =		%
IM ‖‖‖ ‖‖‖ ‖‖‖ ‖‖‖ ‖‖‖ ‖‖‖ ‖‖‖ ‖‖‖		÷ 128 X 100 =		
EV ‖‖‖ ‖				
CC				

3. Next, total the rows in each table to determine the number of questions you answered incorrectly in each category.

4. Then, calculate the percentage of questions you answered incorrectly for each category. To calculate the percentage, divide the number of questions you answered incorrectly by the total number of questions for that category (found at the end of the row) and multiply by 100 (see Sample —Steps 3&4).

SAMPLE — STEPS 3&4
PERFORMANCE PROFILE TALLY SHEET

TABLE A: COMPETENCY CATEGORY

CATEGORY	TOTAL INCORRECT	% INCORRECT
DC $\cancel{HHH}$ $\cancel{HHH}$	10 ÷ 19 X 100 =	52 %
AI ////	4 ÷ 17 X 100 =	23 %
PC $\cancel{HHH}$ $\cancel{HHH}$ //	12 ÷ 20 X 100 =	60 %
IM $\cancel{HHH}$ $\cancel{HHH}$ $\cancel{HHH}$ $\cancel{HHH}$ $\cancel{HHH}$ $\cancel{HHH}$ $\cancel{HHH}$ $\cancel{HHH}$	40 ÷ 128 X 100 =	
EV $\cancel{HHH}$ //		

5. Your performance profile can now be created by taking the percentage values from each category and darkening the corresponding rows on the Performance Profile Chart (see Sample — Step 5).

SAMPLE — STEP 5
PERFORMANCE PROFILE CHART

TABLE A: COMPETENCY CATEGORY

% OF INCORRECT ANSWERS

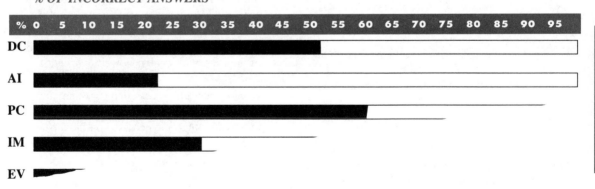

| % 0 | 5 | 10 | 15 | 20 | 25 | 30 | 35 | 40 | 45 | 50 | 55 | 60 | 65 | 70 | 75 | 80 | 85 | 90 | 95 |

INTERPRETATION OF PERFORMANCE

The goal in creating your Performance Profile is to identify your areas of relative strength and weakness. This information can help you in making the best use of your remaining preparation time.

Competency Category Results

Generally, those categories in which you selected a high percentage of incorrect answers are the areas you should focus on during your remaining preparation time. However, this approach can be refined somewhat to arrive at a more accurate diagnosis.

In looking at the TOTAL column of each table on the tally sheets, you will notice that the number of questions in each category varies; some areas have relatively few questions whereas other have many. This is an important aspect in understanding your performance. Both the percentage of incorrect responses in a category and the total number of incorrect responses in a category should be carefully considered to make a complete interpretation of your performance.

You will recall that the Competency Category is a weighted element of the examination *Blueprint*. This means that the number of questions on the exam from each competency category is set and that this number is not equal for each category. The distribution of questions on the Practice Exam, by category, is as follows:

– Data Collection 19 questions

– Analysis and Interpretation of Data 17 questions

– Planning Care 20 questions

– Implementation 128 questions

– Evaluation 14 questions

– Collaboration and Coordination 8 questions

– Professional Practice 52 questions

The following example will help to illustrate the importance of considering both the percentage and the number of incorrect responses in a category. If your profile chart shows that you selected the highest percentage of incorrect answers in the Collaboration and Coordination category in Table A, you should keep in mind that a relatively small number of questions on the exam deal with Collaboration and Coordination (i.e., approximately 8 questions out of the total of 258). Even if you selected only correct responses for that category, the impact on your total score would be small. On the other hand, a fairly low percentage of incorrect responses in the Implementation category (with as many as 128 questions out of the total 258) can represent many questions on the exam. Consequently, improving your performance in this category by only a few percentage marks can make a greater difference overall.

Therefore, although a high percentage of incorrect responses in a competency category is certainly an indication of a weakness in that category, your best strategy for studying may require you to focus in another category, one that has a greater representation on the exam.

Once you have determined which competency categories you need to improve in, you may wish to follow the three steps below:

1. Go to Appendix A and review the competencies in the categories identified as areas of weakness for you; this will give you an overview of the competencies that require your attention.

2. Review the questions that are classified in the competency categories you have identified as weaker for you. Include in your review both the questions you answered correctly as well as those you answered incorrectly; this will give a more complete review of the content that measures the competencies you need to work on. Be sure to read the rationales for the correct and incorrect responses to get a better understanding of your areas of weakness.

3. Look up the references cited (or other comparable references) for the questions you answered incorrectly; this can increase your understanding of material you may not have yet fully mastered.

Nursing Practice Results

The interpretation given for the competency categories does not apply to the Nursing Practice categories because they do not represent a weighted element of the *Blueprint*. This means that all forms or versions of the exam are prepared without consideration of the Nursing Practice classification; the distribution of questions across the Nursing Practice categories can vary with each form or version of the exam.

This makes the interpretation of your results simpler. The best way to interpret your results is to focus on the percentage of incorrect responses by category as shown on the Performance Profile Chart. The categories with the highest percentages of incorrect responses are those on which you should focus your attention.

As a strategy for dealing with your identified area(s) of weakness in the Nursing Practice categories, you may wish to follow the three steps below:

1. Verify your understanding of the categories that are causing difficulties for you. This can be done by reviewing the definition of these categories which are provided earlier in this chapter.

2. Review all the questions that have been classified in your weaker categories. Include the questions that you answered correctly as well as those you answered incorrectly. This will provide for a more complete review of the categories in question.

3. Look up the references cited (or other comparable references) to review the more detailed information they will offer on the content with which you had difficulty.

Finally, you can retake the Practice Exam after having completed your review and preparation. By following the suggested strategies for dealing with your results, you should see an improvement in your overall score as well as in your Performance Profile results.

6

CHAPTER 7

7

Rationales for Practice Exam Questions

BOOK

1

Rationales

CASE 1

1 CORRECT ANSWER: 2

1. Offering Mrs. Kowalski printed information on weight reduction is not the best approach because the nurse should review the information with the client. Also, printed information may not be appropriate because of the possible language barrier.
2. Discussing Mrs. Kowalski's food preferences with her and the dietitian is appropriate because the nurse is involving the client in the decision-making process.
3. Mrs. Kowalski's favorite foods may be high in calories and, therefore, not appropriate for weight reduction.
4. Although obesity will aggravate the osteoarthritis, this choice does not address the issue of menu planning.

CLASSIFICATION

Competency Category:	Implementation
Taxonomic Level:	Application
Client Age:	Older Adult
Nursing Practice:	Physiological Needs

REFERENCES
Craven & Hirnle (1992), pp. 916-917
Potter & Perry (1993), p. 189

2 CORRECT ANSWER: 3

1. This is a possible route of administration but cannot be used by the nurse without the physician's order.
2. Constipation is not an adverse reaction to indomethacin while diarrhea is. A laxative may be harmful.
3. GI upset is a side effect of indomethacin. This can be reduced by taking the medication with food.
4. If the present dose is giving Mrs. Kowalski relief from the pain and stiffness in her joints, reducing the dose to deal with the GI upset would be counter-productive.

CLASSIFICATION

Competency Category:	Implementation
Taxonomic Level:	Application
Client Age:	Older Adult
Nursing Practice:	Pharmacology

REFERENCES
Craven & Hirnle (1992), pp. 521-523
Skidmore-Roth (1993), pp. 508-509

3 CORRECT ANSWER: 1

1. Isometric exercises are the best type of exercise because they improve circulation without inflaming the joints.
2. Passive range-of-motion exercises may increase inflammation and pain.
3. With the pain associated with the acute phase of her osteoarthritis, it is unrealistic to expect that Mrs. Kowalski would be able to perform all activities of daily living.
4. Mrs. Kowalski is unlikely to be able to tolerate walking in her present condition.

CLASSIFICATION

Competency Category:	Implementation
Taxonomic Level:	Critical Thinking
Client Age:	Older Adult
Nursing Practice:	Physiological Needs

REFERENCES

Carnevali & Patrick (1993), pp. 601-603
Eliopoulos (1993), p. 225

4 CORRECT ANSWER: 1

1. This sequence of activities allows for ample rest/activity/relaxation.
2. Clients with osteoarthritis need plenty of time to become active in the morning. As well, there should be some activity between the soaks and bed rest.
3. Analgesics should be administered prior to stress-inducing activities.
4. The exercise program should not be scheduled close to lunch because Mrs. Kowalski will need time for rest.

CLASSIFICATION

Competency Category:	Implementation
Taxonomic Level:	Critical Thinking
Client Age:	Older Adult
Nursing Practice:	Physiological Needs

REFERENCES

Birchenall & Streight (1993), pp. 208-213
Eliopoulos (1993), pp. 224-225

5 CORRECT ANSWER: 4

1. Although a wrist splint will rest and support the joint, it will not assist in total body alignment.
2. The analgesic will help Mrs. Kowalski to sleep, but will not necessarily help with body alignment.
3. Lightweight but warm clothing will help to ease discomfort, but is not a direct means of promoting body alignment.
4. Placing the pillow between her knees will help to maintain alignment, prevent contractures, and facilitate circulation.

CLASSIFICATION

Competency Category:	Implementation
Taxonomic Level:	Application
Client Age:	Older Adult
Nursing Practice:	Clinical Techniques

REFERENCES

Birchenall & Streight (1993), p. 210
Eliopoulos (1993), pp. 322-324

6 CORRECT ANSWER: 2

1. Dance therapy may promote group movement/dynamics, but is too narrow a focus.
2. Rehabilitation would not have been a focus on the nurse's previous unit; therefore it would be a necessary focus in this setting.
3. The nurse would have worked with auxiliary personnel in the previous setting and this would not be a primary need.
4. It is unlikely that Mrs. Kowalski will be discharged any time soon, if at all; although community resources are important to know, they would not be needed immediately.

CLASSIFICATION

Competency Category:	Professional Practice
Taxonomic Level:	Application
Client Age:	Older Adult
Nursing Practice:	Professional Responsibilities

REFERENCES

Ebersole & Hess (1990), p. 766
Eliopoulos (1993), pp. 411-414

CASE 2

7 CORRECT ANSWER: 3

1. Palpating the acromion process is the method used to locate the site of the deltoid muscle.
2. Dividing the femur into thirds is the method used to locate the site of the vastus lateralis muscle.
3. Identifying the greater trochanter of the femur is the method used to locate the site of the ventrogluteal muscle.
4. Palpating the posterosuperior iliac spine is the method used to locate the site of the dorsogluteal muscle.

CLASSIFICATION

Competency Category:	Implementation
Taxonomic Level:	Knowledge/Comprehension
Client Age:	Adult
Nursing Practice:	Pharmacology

REFERENCES

Kozier et al. (1991), pp. 1279-1282
Potter & Perry (1993), pp. 660-661

8 CORRECT ANSWER: 2

1. A position with the client's head raised 45° would not relieve pressure on the vena cava.
2. The weight of the uterus and fetus lying on the vena cava obstruct venous return from the extremities. The client should be repositioned to reduce the supine hypotension.
3. The client is experiencing supine hypotension and should not be kept in a supine position.
4. Blood flow from the extremities would still be obstructed if the client were in the knee-chest position.

CLASSIFICATION

Competency Category:	Implementation
Taxonomic Level:	Application
Client Age:	Adult
Nursing Practice:	Clinical Techniques

REFERENCES

Olds et al. (1992), p. 662
Reeder et al. (1992), p. 482

9 CORRECT ANSWER: 3

1. A gown is necessary only if clothing can become contaminated by fluids being splashed.
2. To avoid needle-stick injuries, the nurse should dispose of equipment in a puncture-resistant container. Recapping needles is an unsafe practice.
3. Universal precautions are necessary when dealing with vaginal or seminal secretions. Wearing gloves is necessary.
4. Masks are necessary only when there is a risk of contaminated fluids being splashed.

CLASSIFICATION

Competency Category:	Implementation
Taxonomic Level:	Knowledge/Comprehension
Client Age:	Adult
Nursing Practice:	Clinical Techniques

REFERENCES

Kozier et al. (1991), pp. 472-474
Potter & Perry (1993), pp. 422-423

10 CORRECT ANSWER: 1

1. Postpartum hemorrhage requires emergency measures such as placing the client in the shock position and notifying the physician.
2. Notifying the nursing supervisor does nothing to stop the bleeding.
3. Fowler's position does not help to control hemorrhage.
4. The client is demonstrating signs of shock. Massaging the fundus is a proper intervention for boggy uterus, but there is no data to support this as the cause of shock.

CLASSIFICATION

Competency Category:	Evaluation
Taxonomic Level:	Critical Thinking
Client Age:	Adult
Nursing Practice:	Physiological Needs

REFERENCES

Olds et al. (1992), p. 684
Smeltzer & Bare (1992), p. 461

11 CORRECT ANSWER: 2

1. When the client shares information with the supervisor, there is no guarantee that the information will be given to Nurse Smith.
2. Relating the client's comment directly to the nurse promotes collegiality between nurses and rewards Nurse Smith for a job well done.
3. Encouraging the client to record her comments on the evaluation form assumes that the form will be completed and that Nurse Smith will be informed of the comments.
4. Reporting the client's comment to the supervisor does not ensure the information is recorded and relayed to Nurse Smith.

CLASSIFICATION

Competency Category:	Professional Practice
Taxonomic Level:	Affective
Client Age:	Adult
Nursing Practice:	Professional Responsibilities

REFERENCES

Arnold & Boggs (1989), p. 375
Ellis & Hartley (1992), p. 218

CASE 3

12 CORRECT ANSWER: 3

1. Being an only child would not be pertinent because bacterial meningitis is a communicable disease.
2. Playing outdoors daily would not contribute to the spread of infection.
3. Bacterial meningitis is transmitted by droplet infection from nasopharyngeal secretions. Children of this age group often have poor handwashing techniques and share toys leading to the spread of infection.
4. The risk of contracting or spreading the bacteria is minimal in the adult population.

CLASSIFICATION

Competency Category:	Analysis & Interpretation of Data
Taxonomic Level:	Critical Thinking
Client Age:	Child & Adolescent
Nursing Practice:	Screening & Diagnosis

REFERENCES
Foster et al. (1989), p. 1759
Whaley & Wong (1993), p. 961

13 CORRECT ANSWER: 4

1. Decreased activity is nondescript and needs to be supported by facts. Vomiting is an incomplete statement and requires further data to be included.
2. Nursing entries need to describe actual behaviors that the nurse has observed (i.e., seen, heard, smelled, or felt). The term "irritable" is a judgment and needs to be supported by facts.
3. Charting must be precise and accurate. The actual temperature needs to be recorded. "Complaining" is a nondescript term; what the child actually says and how she behaves is more accurate.
4. The description "face flushed" is accurate as it describes what the nurse has seen. The actual behavior the child has demonstrated (i.e., crying with position changes) is documented.

CLASSIFICATION

Competency Category:	Data Collection
Taxonomic Level:	Application
Client Age:	Child & Adolescent
Nursing Practice:	Professional Responsibilities

REFERENCES
Craven & Hirnle (1992), pp. 150-154
Potter & Perry (1993), pp. 696-700

14 CORRECT ANSWER: 1

1. It is imperative that those individuals who have been exposed to Roberta in the past week be contacted so that prophylaxis treatment can be initiated.
2. Bacterial meningitis requires respiratory isolation because it is spread by droplet infection. Isolation is only required for 48 hours once antibiotic therapy has been implemented.
3. It is a medical responsibility to inform the parents of the complications of bacterial meningitis. The nurse's responsibility would be to support the parents, not to inform them.
4. Because bacterial meningitis is transmitted by droplets, cleanliness is important. Roberta's utensils and bedding should be clean, but there is no need to sterilize them.

CLASSIFICATION

Competency Category:	Implementation
Taxonomic Level:	Application
Client Age:	Child & Adolescent
Nursing Practice:	Clinical Techniques

REFERENCES
Jackson & Saunders (1993), p. 1390
Whaley & Wong (1993), p. 963

15 CORRECT ANSWER: 4

1. Hourly assessments of the I.V. should be done to identify potential problems. Therefore, no corrective action is necessary.
2. I.V. infusion pumps allow the exact amount of fluid to be infused and provide an alarm when the pressure in the vein increases, thus identifying interstitial I.V. and potential problems. Therefore, no corrective action is required.
3. The insertion site should be covered with a transparent dressing to allow for observation of the site. Therefore, no corrective action is required.
4. Small children require varying degrees of immobilization when they have an I.V. The affected limb should be on an arm board at all times. This prevents the cannula from dislodging and causing injury to the child.

CLASSIFICATION

Competency Category:	Evaluation
Taxonomic Level:	Application
Client Age:	Child & Adolescent
Nursing Practice:	Clinical Techniques

REFERENCES
Jackson & Saunders (1993), pp. 578-579
Whaley & Wong (1993), pp. 687-688

16 CORRECT ANSWER: 3

1. Although it is important for a 2-year-old to interact with others, it is more important to decrease activity and sensory stimulation for children affected with bacterial meningitis
2. Parents are encouraged to visit as often, and for as long as they wish, to reduce separation anxiety. The child will likely sleep and be subdued while parents are present.
3. Grouping of interventions allows for minimal handling as children with bacterial meningitis are hypersensitive to noise and handling.
4. Environmental stimuli should be kept to a minimum because children affected with bacterial meningitis are sensitive to lighting and other environmental stimuli.

CLASSIFICATION

Competency Category:	Implementation
Taxonomic Level:	Application
Client Age:	Child & Adolescent
Nursing Practice:	Physiological Needs

REFERENCES

Jackson & Saunders (1993), p. 1390
Whaley & Wong (1993), p. 963

17 CORRECT ANSWER: 2

1. There should be no reason to keep Roberta home. There has been disruption within the family and it is important to normalize home routines.
2. Hearing loss from pressure on the eighth cranial nerve is a relatively common complication of bacterial meningitis and should be followed up after discharge.
3. Dental problems are not a sequela of meningitis.
4. There is no indication that a referral to a dietitian would be necessary for this child. It is not a specific requirement for follow-up to bacterial meningitis.

CLASSIFICATION

Competency Category:	Implementation
Taxonomic Level:	Application
Client Age:	Child & Adolescent
Nursing Practice:	Physiological Needs

REFERENCES

Foster et al. (1989), p. 1762
Jackson & Saunders (1993), p. 1390

CASE 4

18 CORRECT ANSWER: 3

1. A supine position would increase abdominal pressure on the diaphragm and make breathing more difficult.
2. The recovery position would increase abdominal pressure on the diaphragm and increase movement of fluids into upper airways.
3. High-Fowler's is the position of choice when breathing is difficult. It decreases abdominal pressure on the diaphragm and permits optimal chest expansion.
4. There is no rationale for placing the client on one side over the other as this would favor the expansion of one lung over the other which is contraindicated in acute asthma.

CLASSIFICATION

Competency Category:	Implementation
Taxonomic Level:	Knowledge/Comprehension
Client Age:	Adult
Nursing Practice:	Clinical Techniques

REFERENCES

Kozier et al. (1991), p. 1105
Lewis & Collier (1992), p. 575

19 CORRECT ANSWER: 1

1. Strong and new odors such as paint fumes are frequent triggers of an asthma attack.
2. Exposure to crowds is not a trigger for asthma, although the potential for developing an upper respiratory infection may be increased.
3. A pet with which the client has had ongoing contact is not likely to become a trigger for asthma.
4. Although trees and plants represent a potential trigger for asthma, adults are not likely to experience an asthma attack when exposed to these objects in a wide open space such as a garden.

CLASSIFICATION

Competency Category:	Data Collection
Taxonomic Level:	Application
Client Age:	Adult
Nursing Practice:	Screening & Diagnosis

REFERENCES

Black & Matassarin-Jabocs (1993), p. 1022
Smeltzer & Bare (1992), p. 578

20 CORRECT ANSWER: 2

1. Shortness of breath, decreased activity, and medication may contribute to a decrease in appetite. Therefore, decreased appetite is not unexpected given Mrs. Bells' situation, and is not the most important finding to be shared at the end-of-shift report.
2. Increased restlessness is an early indication of hypoxia and should be reported so that it may be followed up.
3. Increased urinary output is not directly related to Mrs. Bells' respiratory status, which is the most critical element to be assessed and reported.
4. Generalized expiratory wheezing is a normal finding in a client experiencing an acute asthma attack. This does not alert the nurse to an oncoming problem.

CLASSIFICATION

Competency Category:	Collaboration & Coordination
Taxonomic Level:	Critical Thinking
Client Age:	Adult
Nursing Practice:	Professional Responsibilities

REFERENCES
Lewis & Collier (1992), p. 574
Smeltzer & Bare (1992), p. 583

21 CORRECT ANSWER: 1

1. Waiting 30 seconds between puffs allows time for valve pressure to rebuild. The first puff dilates the bronchus so that the medication is well absorbed during the second puff.
2. The client should exhale, not inhale, before taking the first puff.
3. The mouthpiece should be closer than 15 cm from the mouth.
4. The canister should be shaken and rotated before and between puffs.

CLASSIFICATION

Competency Category:	Implementation
Taxonomic Level:	Application
Client Age:	Adult
Nursing Practice:	Pharmacology

REFERENCES
Kozier et al. (1991), p. 1108
Lewis & Collier (1992), p. 570

22 CORRECT ANSWER: 4

1. It is appropriate for the client to have ready access to the inhalers at all times.
2. Using the bronchodilator inhaler increases the absorption and effectiveness of the anti-inflammatory medication.
3. Throat irritation is an expected side effect of anti-inflammatory inhalers.
4. An anti-inflammatory inhaler is not effective during an acute attack because the client is in bronchospasm and the medication cannot be inhaled.

CLASSIFICATION

Competency Category:	Implementation
Taxonomic Level:	Application
Client Age:	Adult
Nursing Practice:	Pharmacology

REFERENCES
Baer & Williams (1992), p. 76
Lewis & Collier (1992), p. 570

23 CORRECT ANSWER: 3

1. The client is an individual. Suggesting the client is like most people (who can manage their asthma) is condescending and may be dishonest.
2. Suggesting the client's proximity to the hospital is beneficial supports the client's dependency on the health care system, negates the client's feelings, and prevents further exploration of concerns.
3. Suggesting the client may be admitted from time to time honestly addresses the client's concern, is sincere, and offers hope that she will receive help.
4. Suggesting the physician will develop a medication regimen does not guarantee the client will not have further admissions.

CLASSIFICATION

Competency Category: Professional Practice
Taxonomic Level: Affective
Client Age: Adult
Nursing Practice: Communication

REFERENCES

Arnold & Boggs (1989), p. 254
Smith (1992), p. 67

CASE 5

24 CORRECT ANSWER: 3

1. A barium enema is a test of the large intestine, not the small intestine.
2. A barium enema is a diagnostic test to visualize the large bowel; it will not open an obstruction.
3. A barium enema is administered to visualize the large intestine and to identify the presence of a blockage.
4. A barium enema is not used to cleanse the bowel. Barium may be difficult to excrete and can cause constipation.

CLASSIFICATION

Competency Category: Implementation
Taxonomic Level: Application
Client Age: Adult
Nursing Practice: Screening & Diagnosis

REFERENCES

Black & Matassarin-Jabocs (1993), p. 1566
Lewis & Collier (1992), p. 967

25 CORRECT ANSWER: 2

1. The nurse cannot plan what teaching strategies will be used until the learning needs have been identified. Perhaps reading will not be required.
2. The first step in client teaching is to assess the learning needs of the client.
3. The nurse does not begin teaching until the learning needs have been identified.
4. Until the client knows what the content of the teaching session will be, he may not know whether he wants his wife with him.

CLASSIFICATION

Competency Category: Implementation
Taxonomic Level: Application
Client Age: Adult
Nursing Practice: Communication

REFERENCES

Kozier et al. (1991), p. 284
Redman (1993), p. 10

26 CORRECT ANSWER: 4

1. Administering medications is a dependent nursing function. Nurses must follow the order as written by the physician.
2. Dividing the dose is incorrect because the nurse must follow the order as it is written by the physician.
3. Part of the nurse's responsibility for administration of medications is to check the client's readiness for medication. It is inappropriate to make him wait in pain until the medication order can be followed.
4. Notifying the physician is correct as the client is in need of more medication and the nurse cannot administer additional medication without another order from the physician.

CLASSIFICATION
Competency Category:	Professional Practice
Taxonomic Level:	Application
Client Age:	Adult
Nursing Practice:	Pharmacology

REFERENCES
Ellis & Hartley (1992), pp. 138-139
Wilson & Kneisl (1992), p. 3

27 CORRECT ANSWER: 3

1. Placing soiled linen in an isolation bag is incorrect because, with universal precautions, there are no isolation bags for laundry. Any health care worker handling soiled linen is expected to wear gloves and gowns if necessary.
2. Checking the chart for HIV and hepatitis test results is incorrect because universal precautions are practiced with all clients, not just those with positive test results.
3. Wearing gloves is the correct answer because the purpose of universal precautions is to protect the nurse from contact with blood and body fluids.
4. While it is correct to use sterile technique to change his abdominal dressing, this technique is not classified under universal precautions.

CLASSIFICATION
Competency Category:	Implementation
Taxonomic Level:	Knowledge/Comprehension
Client Age:	Adult
Nursing Practice:	Physiological Needs

REFERENCES
Black & Matassarin-Jabocs (1993), p. 553
Phipps et al. (1991), p. 294

28 CORRECT ANSWER: 1

1. Transferring the client to a functioning bed is correct because it meets the nurse's responsibility to reduce environmental hazards.
2. Helping the client out of bed with the bed in the raised position is incorrect because it puts the client at risk of falling, especially when getting up for the first time with an abdominal incision.
3. Using a footstool increases the risk of a fall as this is the client's first time out of bed postoperatively.
4. Propping the client in bed with pillows and keeping the side rails in place would promote safety for the moment, but these actions do not address the problem with the bed.

CLASSIFICATION

Competency Category:	Implementation
Taxonomic Level:	Critical Thinking
Client Age:	Adult
Nursing Practice:	Physiological Needs

REFERENCES

Potter & Perry (1993), pp. 1439-1440

Taylor et al. (1993), pp. 495-496

29 CORRECT ANSWER: 3

1. Assessing his anxiety level will do nothing to reduce his incisional pain. More direct intervention is necessary.
2. He may be unable to rest if he is experiencing incisional pain. Getting him up will likely increase his pain.
3. Positioning him on his side with his knees flexed and a pillow between his legs will lessen the strain on his abdominal muscles and the sutures.
4. Reassuring him that some pain is to be expected and that it will get better does nothing to help him deal with his present pain.

CLASSIFICATION

Competency Category:	Implementation
Taxonomic Level:	Application
Client Age:	Adult
Nursing Practice:	Clinical Techniques

REFERENCES

Ignatavicius & Bayne (1991), pp. 484-485

Smeltzer & Bare (1992), p. 440

CASE 6

30 CORRECT ANSWER: 3

1. Although the role of caffeine in hypertension is controversial, one cup of coffee a day is not considered excessive.
2. Because alcohol may raise blood pressure, moderate consumption is advised. The consumption described is not significant with respect to hypertension.
3. Nicotine constricts blood vessels, therefore elevating her BP.
4. A family history of prostatic cancer would not increase the risk of hypertension.

CLASSIFICATION

Competency Category:	Implementation
Taxonomic Level:	Application
Client Age:	Adult
Nursing Practice:	Screening & Diagnosis

REFERENCES

Phipps et al. (1991), p. 765
Smeltzer & Bare (1992), p. 757

31 CORRECT ANSWER: 3

1. There is no indication that Mrs. Rogers will be uncooperative with her treatment.
2. Data collected at this point does not support the hypothesis that Mrs. Rogers is coping ineffectively.
3. Alteration in nutrition is the high-priority nursing diagnosis given that she has a high fat and salt intake, potentiating hypertension and obesity.
4. Excess salt intake would result in a fluid volume excess.

CLASSIFICATION

Competency Category:	Analysis & Interpretation of Data
Taxonomic Level:	Application
Client Age:	Adult
Nursing Practice:	Screening & Diagnosis

REFERENCES

Phipps et al. (1991), p. 770
Smeltzer & Bare (1992), pp. 764-765

32 CORRECT ANSWER: 4

1. The potassium level is elevated, and should be normal (3.5-5.5 mEq/L), or could be decreased, with the use of chlorothiazide (Diuril).
2. Mrs. Rogers' BP remains unchanged and chlorothiazide (Diuril) should lower her BP.
3. Mrs. Rogers' weight should decrease as diuresis occurs.
4. An overall deficit indicates diuresis, an expected outcome with chlorothiazide (Diuril).

CLASSIFICATION

Competency Category:	Implementation
Taxonomic Level:	Application
Client Age:	Adult
Nursing Practice:	Pharmacology

REFERENCES

Black & Matassarin-Jabocs (1993), p. 1275
Phipps et al. (1991), pp. 768-769

33 CORRECT ANSWER: 3

1. Nurse Smith is demonstrating insecurity and is being defensive.
2. By stating what has happened in the past, Nurse Smith is being defensive.
3. By agreeing to try sample menus, Nurse Smith is indicating a receptiveness to new ideas.
4. It is within the nurse's scope of practice to provide sample menus to a client without the dietitian's help.

CLASSIFICATION

Competency Category:	Professional Practice
Taxonomic Level:	Affective
Client Age:	Adult
Nursing Practice:	Professional Responsibilities

REFERENCES
Craven & Hirnle (1992), p. 62
McClosky & Grace (1990), pp. 51-52

34 CORRECT ANSWER: 3

1. Stating that "It's only a blood pressure" devalues the importance of the constructive feedback and indicates that Nurse Jones does not understand the importance of BP assessment in relation to antihypertensives.
2. Defensively stating "I already knew that" implies BP assessment is not important.
3. Stating "I must remember that" and asking if blood pressure needs to be taken prior to administering antihypertensive medication indicate acceptance of constructive feedback.
4. Not checking the blood pressure because it is in the normal range shows a lack of knowledge regarding antihypertensive medications.

CLASSIFICATION

Competency Category:	Professional Practice
Taxonomic Level:	Affective
Client Age:	Adult
Nursing Practice:	Professional Responsibilities

REFERENCES
Arnold & Boggs (1989), pp. 5, 251, 253
Craven & Hirnle (1992), p. 63

CASE 7

35 CORRECT ANSWER: 3

1. When the child sits upright, gravity facilitates drainage from only the upper segments and bronchi.
2. A supine position is used to promote drainage from only the anterior lobes.
3. Frequent changes of position are recommended during postural drainage and percussion to facilitate drainage from all major lung segments.
4. Positioning the child with the chest lower than the abdomen is used to remove secretions from only the lower lobes and bronchi.

CLASSIFICATION

Competency Category:	Implementation
Taxonomic Level:	Knowledge/Comprehension
Client Age:	Child & Adolescent
Nursing Practice:	Clinical Techniques

REFERENCES
Pillitteri (1992), pp. 1202-1203
Whaley & Wong (1993), p. 692

36 CORRECT ANSWER: 4

1. Discussing the techniques for postural drainage may not address the specific needs of the learner. The parents may understand the treatment but require assistance in adapting their approach to make it more acceptable to the child.
2. Postural drainage treatments are critical to the daily management of cystic fibrosis. Due to the chronic nature of the illness, it is necessary that family members are actively involved in the treatment.
3. Postural drainage and percussion are important aspects of the treatment and should be done 2-4 times daily, to prevent infection. Delaying treatment will increase the risk of respiratory infections.
4. Teaching should be individualized to address the specific needs of the learner once they have been assessed.

CLASSIFICATION

Competency Category:	Implementation
Taxonomic Level:	Application
Client Age:	Child & Adolescent
Nursing Practice:	Communication

REFERENCES

Foster et al. (1989), pp. 1246-1249
Kozier et al. (1991), pp. 281-284

37 CORRECT ANSWER: 4

1. The Apgar score is used immediately after birth to evaluate the newborn's adjustment to extrauterine life.
2. The Snellen Screening Test is used to measure visual acuity.
3. An Intelligence Quotient test measures cognitive ability.
4. The Denver Developmental Screening Test is a widely used screening test which evaluates personal/social, fine motor, language, and gross motor skills in children from 2 weeks to 6 years of age.

CLASSIFICATION

Competency Category:	Data Collection
Taxonomic Level:	Knowledge/Comprehension
Client Age:	Child & Adolescent
Nursing Practice:	Screening & Diagnosis

REFERENCES

Foster et al. (1989), pp. 1040-1041
Whaley & Wong (1993), pp. 169, 182

38 CORRECT ANSWER: 4

1. Watching the child prepare all his medications puts unreasonably high expectations and responsibility on a 4-year-old.
2. Telling the child to describe to his mother the pathology of cystic fibrosis is inappropriate; it is unreasonable to expect a 4-year-old to understand and explain the pathology of a disease.
3. Asking the child if he understands everything that has been taught is not effective in getting him to demonstrate whether learning has occurred. The nurse should use an open-ended means of communication.
4. Asking the child to point out different areas for chest physiotherapy on his doll allows him to recall basic facts and to use something tangible and familiar to demonstrate his knowledge. The nurse must consider the growth and development level of the child.

CLASSIFICATION

Competency Category:	Implementation
Taxonomic Level:	Application
Client Age:	Child & Adolescent
Nursing Practice:	Communication

REFERENCES
Foster et al. (1989), p. 796
Kozier et al. (1991), p. 293

39 CORRECT ANSWER: 3

1. Constipation indicates a need for fewer enzymes which the mother is meeting by decreasing the amount administered.
2. It is recommended that pancreatic enzymes be increased to match food intake; therefore, further teaching is unnecessary.
3. Tyler's mother needs additional teaching so that she is instructed to administer pancreatic enzymes with all meals and snacks rather than only in the morning and at bedtime.
4. Tyler's mother is correct in increasing the enzymes since large, bulky stools are suggestive of impaired absorption. This does not suggest a need for additional teaching.

CLASSIFICATION

Competency Category:	Analysis & Interpretation of Data
Taxonomic Level:	Application
Client Age:	Child & Adolescent
Nursing Practice:	Screening & Diagnosis

REFERENCES
Foster et al. (1989), pp.1246-1249
Whaley & Wong (1993), pp. 744-746

40 CORRECT ANSWER: 4

1. Mrs. Jones' reaction is a normal response. Many parents who have children with a chronic illness experience "chronic sorrow"; that is, times when parental sorrow and grief resurface. The nurse should not assume or tell the client she is depressed.
2. Telling the family they are coping well belittles their concern by providing false reassurance.
3. Research has shown that after 1 year, many families do find living with cystic fibrosis less stressful. The nurse needs to recognize that each family may react somewhat differently and not compare Tyler's parents with "most people."
4. Social support may help decrease feelings of isolation. Families who share their burden with family members or other helpers outside the family tend to demonstrate higher levels of family functioning.

CLASSIFICATION

Competency Category:	Collaboration & Coordination
Taxonomic Level:	Application
Client Age:	Child & Adolescent
Nursing Practice:	Psychosocial Needs

REFERENCES

Foster et al. (1989), pp. 741-743
Mott et al. (1990), p. 633

41 CORRECT ANSWER: 2

1. The nurse needs a policy approved by the nurse's employing agency, not by an external agency such as the local hospital.
2. When the nurse is assigned to work outside an area of present competence, the nurse's immediate supervisor should be contacted for direction.
3. Carrying out the procedure is wrong because it could result in injury to the client.
4. The lack of a policy should be discussed at the local level initially before contacting a provincial/territorial association.

CLASSIFICATION

Competency Category:	Professional Practice
Taxonomic Level:	Application
Client Age:	Child & Adolescent
Nursing Practice:	Professional Responsibilities

REFERENCES

Canadian Nurses Association (1991), p. 9
Morris (1991), p. 120

CASE 8

42 CORRECT ANSWER: 1

1. Sexual assault victims are particularly sensitized to being touched against their will (this is the nature of violation) and need to regain the feeling that they can choose when they will be touched.
2. Provision of privacy with the company of one other person is preferred over large groups.
3. Encouraging sexual assault victims to make decisions, however minor, helps them to regain a sense of control and power over what is happening to them.
4. Legal terminology depersonalizes the experience and may make the client think she is being judged as to the truth of her claim.

CLASSIFICATION

Competency Category:	Implementation
Taxonomic Level:	Knowledge/Comprehension
Client Age:	Adult
Nursing Practice:	Psychosocial Needs

REFERENCES
Fogel & Lauver (1990), pp. 532-535
Johnson (1993), p. 683

43 CORRECT ANSWER: 1

1. This statement acknowledges the client's pain but encourages her to tell her story. This demonstration of empathy, warmth, and respect is therapeutic and vital to her plan of care.
2. This statement may be interpreted by the client as a threat.
3. Direct questioning can be very threatening.
4. This statement is condescending in nature and removes control from the client.

CLASSIFICATION

Competency Category:	Implementation
Taxonomic Level:	Affective
Client Age:	Adult
Nursing Practice:	Communication

REFERENCES
Beck et al. (1993), pp. 688-692
Fogel & Lauver (1990), pp. 532-535

44 CORRECT ANSWER: 3

1. Any washing may remove important evidence such as foreign tissue under her nails.
2. It is not necessary for the victim to notify the police immediately. Jackie can decide to prosecute at a later time, provided the necessary evidence is collected before she bathes.
3. Specific procedures must be followed before bathing to ensure Jackie has the option to press charges.
4. Tests are required to collect necessary evidence as well as to detect disease. Prophylaxis may be given after all tests are completed and before diagnosis is confirmed.

CLASSIFICATION

Competency Category:	Implementation
Taxonomic Level:	Application
Client Age:	Adult
Nursing Practice:	Screening & Diagnosis

REFERENCES
Beck et al. (1993), pp. 688-692
Fogel & Lauver (1990), pp. 532-535

45 CORRECT ANSWER: 3

1. The physician, not the nurse, would be responsible for inspecting Jackie.
2. Showing the equipment to an adult client is inappropriate.
3. Specific steps and guidelines must be followed in this type of pelvic examination to preserve evidence for legal proceedings. These specifics should be explained to enhance the client's comfort with the procedure.
4. To increase the client's comfort during this invasive procedure, it would be more appropriate for the physician to position Jackie immediately prior to the examination.

CLASSIFICATION

Competency Category:	Implementation
Taxonomic Level:	Application
Client Age:	Adult
Nursing Practice:	Screening & Diagnosis

REFERENCES
Johnson (1993), p. 685
Smeltzer & Bare (1992), pp. 1981-1983

46 CORRECT ANSWER: 1

1. The nurse is acting as an advocate by protecting the client's right to confidentiality.
2. Appraising the client's character and the nature of the situation does not protect the client's right to confidentiality.
3. The circumstances leading to the assault are not relevant to the care of the client and divulging this information is a breach of confidentiality.
4. The nurse is making a judgment as to the accuracy of the client's story, and shows a willingness to discuss confidential information.

CLASSIFICATION

Competency Category:	Professional Practice
Taxonomic Level:	Affective
Client Age:	Adult
Nursing Practice:	Professional Responsibilities

REFERENCES
Canadian Nurses Association (1991), p. 5
Smith (1992), pp. 161-170

47 CORRECT ANSWER: 4

1. The role of ongoing support counselor to sexual assault victims does not fall within the generally accepted scope of nursing practice.
2. Although offering to drive Jackie home may demonstrate concern for the client, it is not within the nurse's scope of practice.
3. Contacting the police to report adult sexual assault must be done with the client's consent, and is not mandatory for the adult client.
4. Drawing blood falls within the scope of nursing practice, if the samples are ordered by a physician. Decreasing the number of personnel with whom the sexual assault victim must interact is considered an important therapeutic action.

CLASSIFICATION

Competency Category:	Professional Practice
Taxonomic Level:	Critical Thinking
Client Age:	Adult
Nursing Practice:	Professional Responsibilities

REFERENCES
Beck et al. (1993), pp. 688-692
Fogel & Lauver (1990), pp. 533-535

INDEPENDENT ITEMS

48 CORRECT ANSWER: 3

1. Children vary greatly in size at different ages; therefore, age it is not appropriate.
2. A nurse is not able to calculate the metabolic rate of the child.
3. Body surface area (BSA) correlates with important physiological factors affecting drug dosages including blood volume, basal metabolic rate, cardiac output, and glomerular filtration.
4. There is no direct percentage relationship between the adult dosage and the pediatric dosage.

CLASSIFICATION

Competency Category:	Implementation
Taxonomic Level:	Knowledge/Comprehension
Client Age:	Child & Adolescent
Nursing Practice:	Pharmacology

REFERENCES

Jackson & Saunders (1993), p. 567
Whaley & Wong (1993), p.671

49 CORRECT ANSWER: 2

1. Hemoglobin is not assessed during transfusion. Tissue turgor is used as an indicator of dehydration.
2. The correct I.V. solution is normal saline. Blood may become more viscous if dextrose solution is used. Vital signs should be monitored.
3. The I.V. for blood must be started with saline. Blood becomes viscous if in contact with a dextrose solution.
4. Urine output need not be checked every 30 minutes. Assessing for hemolytic reaction is an ongoing nursing responsibility.

CLASSIFICATION

Competency Category:	Implementation
Taxonomic Level:	Application
Client Age:	General
Nursing Practice:	Clinical Techniques

REFERENCES

Black & Matassarin-Jabocs (1993), pp. 1391, 1399
Burrell (1992), pp. 567-569, 571

50   CORRECT ANSWER: 4

1. A Sims' position is contraindicated for the client with ascites. Pressure of ascites against the diaphragm will be aggravated by a Sims' position.
2. A prone position is generally contraindicated for the client with ascites. Ascites may produce pressure against the diaphragm, thus hindering diaphragmatic excursion and respirations.
3. A high-Fowler's position would only be indicated for the client with ascites if the client is in respiratory distress.
4. A semi-Fowler's position is indicated for the client with ascites to relieve abdominal pressure against the diaphragm, thus facilitating respiration.

CLASSIFICATION
Competency Category: Implementation
Taxonomic Level: Knowledge/Comprehension
Client Age: General
Nursing Practice: Clinical Techniques

REFERENCES
Black & Matassarin-Jabocs (1993), pp. 1720-1721
Ignatavicius & Bayne (1991), p. 1489

51   CORRECT ANSWER: 4

1. Observation of feeding behaviors between mother and infant does not give the nurse an overall assessment of Angela's learning needs.
2. Performing a baby bath demonstration does not assess Angela's overall learning needs.
3. Angela may be unlikely to articulate her learning needs when faced with a closed question about her knowledge of baby care.
4. Inquiring about Angela's past experience with babies can facilitate the nurse's assessment of Angela's current knowledge and ongoing learning needs.

CLASSIFICATION
Competency Category: Implementation
Taxonomic Level: Application
Client Age: Adult
Nursing Practice: Communication

REFERENCES
Olds et al. (1992), p. 896
Reeder et al. (1992), pp. 321-323

52   CORRECT ANSWER: 3

1. Lorazepam (Ativan) is an anxiolytic and is not indicated for chest pain following a myocardial infarction.
2. Acetominophen, while an analgesic, is not sufficient to relieve chest pain associated with myocardial infarction.
3. Morphine sulfate (Morphine) is an analgesic used to control chest pain associated with a myocardial infarction.
4. Magnesium hydroxide (Maalox) is an antacid and is used for indigestion. It is not indicated for chest pain following a myocardial infarction.

CLASSIFICATION
Competency Category: Implementation
Taxonomic Level: Knowledge/Comprehension
Client Age: General
Nursing Practice: Pharmacology

REFERENCES
Burrell (1992), p. 482
Smeltzer & Bare (1992), p. 652

53 CORRECT ANSWER: 3

1. A red, swollen suture line suggests that it would be unsafe to remove any sutures without notifying the physician.
2. A dressing should be applied when the incision is red and draining. The physician should be notified of the nurse's assessment of the incision.
3. The physician should be notified when an incision is potentially infected. A swab from a red, draining incision should be taken for culture and sensitivity.
4. A hot compress is contraindicated for an inflamed wound.

CLASSIFICATION

Competency Category:	Professional Practice
Taxonomic Level:	Critical Thinking
Client Age:	Adult
Nursing Practice:	Physiological Needs

REFERENCES

Kozier et al. (1991), pp. 1310-1311
Potter & Perry (1993), pp. 1674-1677

54 CORRECT ANSWER: 4

1. A semi-Fowler's position is used for a conscious client. The unconscious client is positioned on his side, facing the nurse; this facilitates drainage of secretions from the pharynx and prevents aspiration.
2. This wall pressure range is too high; it is the range for an adult client, not a child.
3. It is not necessary to use a water-soluble lubricant for oropharyngeal suctioning; the catheter tip can be moistened with sterile water or saline.
4. Applying suction while slowly rotating and withdrawing the catheter ensures the removal of secretions from the surrounding area and prevents trauma to respiratory mucosa.

CLASSIFICATION

Competency Category:	Implementation
Taxonomic Level:	Application
Client Age:	Child & Adolescent
Nursing Practice:	Clinical Techniques

REFERENCES

Foster et al. (1989), p. 1190
Kozier et al. (1991), p. 1117

55 CORRECT ANSWER: 4

1. This question asks Ms. Drake how she feels about herself, not her progress.
2. The answer to this question will not indicate Ms. Drake's view of her progress.
3. The answer to this question could demonstrate Ms. Drake's improvement, but not how she views her progress.
4. This question focuses on Ms. Drake's view of her progress.

CLASSIFICATION

Competency Category:	Evaluation
Taxonomic Level:	Critical Thinking
Client Age:	Older Adult
Nursing Practice:	Communication

REFERENCES

Kozier et al. (1991), pp. 293-294
Potter & Perry (1993), pp. 365-366

56 CORRECT ANSWER: 4

1. A nurse should not be reported for a history of drug dependency if it is not affecting current practice.
2. Unless the inconsistency in following the dress code poses a threat to a client, such an action would not be necessary to report.
3. Although failure to purchase insurance may leave the nurse unprotected, it does not indicate professional misconduct and is not necessary to report.
4. The nurse must protect the client from harm. Failure to follow and meet the professional standards could jeopardize a client's welfare.

CLASSIFICATION

Competency Category:	Professional Practice
Taxonomic Level:	Knowledge/Comprehension
Client Age:	General
Nursing Practice:	Professional Responsibilities

REFERENCES

Canadian Nurses Association (1991), p. 15

Potter & Perry (1993), p. 294

57 CORRECT ANSWER: 4

1. The term "isolated" would need further explanation to the parents.
2. This response has no bearing on Natalie's present infectious condition.
3. The terminology in this response is too technical.
4. This statement is correct because it uses simple terms, and is repetitious to reinforce learning.

CLASSIFICATION

Competency Category:	Implementation
Taxonomic Level:	Application
Client Age:	Child & Adolescent
Nursing Practice:	Communication

REFERENCES

Stanhope & Lancaster (1992), pp. 974-975

Whaley & Wong (1993), pp. 1026-1029

58 CORRECT ANSWER: 1

1. Asking the client what she understands about her condition is the best opening to the admission interview as it allows the client an opportunity to express feelings and to verbalize needs.

2. Suggesting that the client is frightened by the pain is not the best statement to open the interview because it does not allow the client to set the agenda, but instead focuses directly on one issue.

3. While establishing the presence of allergies is important, it would not demonstrate good communication or interviewing technique to start with this question. Using this question makes the nurse set the tone for the interview.

4. The nurse should begin an interview with easily answerable, impersonal questions until a rapport has been established. The nurse should wait for client cues before making assumptions that the client is concerned about a loss of childbearing potential.

CLASSIFICATION

Competency Category:	Data Collection
Taxonomic Level:	Application
Client Age:	Adult
Nursing Practice:	Communication

REFERENCES

Black & Matassarin-Jabocs (1993), p. 165
Potter & Perry (1993), pp. 152-155

59 CORRECT ANSWER: 2

1. If the nurse is not performing the procedure, it is not the nurse's responsibility to inform. However, the nurse does have an obligation to notify the individual performing the procedure that the client is not informed.

2. Acting as a client advocate means acting on the client's behalf to ensure her rights are respected. The nurse must notify the physician who will be performing the procedure that the client is not informed.

3. The responsibility for informing the client regarding a procedure lies with the individual performing the procedure, and not with the family.

4. The nurse from the gastrointestinal clinic is not performing the procedure, and therefore, has no responsibility to inform the client.

CLASSIFICATION

Competency Category:	Professional Practice
Taxonomic Level:	Application
Client Age:	Child & Adolescent
Nursing Practice:	Professional Responsibilities

REFERENCES

Kozier et al. (1991), p. 29
Smeltzer & Bare (1992), p. 13

60 CORRECT ANSWER: 2

1. The nurse should not remove the T-tube. This is a medical competency.
2. The nurse shows awareness of the competency level and professional role for a nurse by telling the physician that T-tube removal is a medical responsibility.
3. The nurse is not responsible for removal of T-tubes.
4. Removal of T-tubes is not a nursing competency.

CLASSIFICATION

Competency Category:	Professional Practice
Taxonomic Level:	Application
Client Age:	Adult
Nursing Practice:	Professional Responsibilities

REFERENCES
Canadian Nurses Association (1991), pp. 9-10
Ellis & Hartley (1992), p. 398

61 CORRECT ANSWER: 2

1. Before assessing the carotid pulse, unresponsiveness must be determined and ventilation provided.
2. Determining unresponsiveness is the first step because the client may be asleep or may have fainted.
3. The need to initiate cardiopulmonary resuscitation must be determined before measures are implemented.
4. The need to initiate cardiopulmonary resuscitation must be determined before measures are implemented.

CLASSIFICATION

Competency Category:	Implementation
Taxonomic Level:	Knowledge/Comprehension
Client Age:	General
Nursing Practice:	Clinical Techniques

REFERENCES
Ignatavicius & Bayne (1991), p. 2140
Kozier et al. (1991), p. 1133

62 CORRECT ANSWER: 3

1. Having a friend learn about the control of diabetes is important, but will not help the client in initial planning for his own care.
2. Teaching about blood glucose monitoring is part of the learning that must occur for a client with diabetes, but at this stage would not be effective because the client has stated that he is overwhelmed.
3. Encouraging Mr. O'Reilly to verbalize his fears and talk with someone who is managing the same illness will support him in beginning to plan for the management of his own illness.
4. Having Mr. O'Reilly read about and understand the different aspects of the disease is important, but may not help him when he is feeling overwhelmed. Also, teaching while in hospital should progress beyond providing pamphlets to read at home.

CLASSIFICATION

Competency Category:	Planning Care
Taxonomic Level:	Application
Client Age:	Adult
Nursing Practice:	Psychosocial Needs

REFERENCES
Guthrie & Guthrie (1991), pp. 319, 323, 324
Kozier et al. (1991), p. 216

63 CORRECT ANSWER: 2

1. Stopping the bed bath is correct, but taking her BP before applying pressure to the dressing is not the priority in this urgent health situation.
2. Staying with the client is critical to provide reassurance and ongoing assessment. Firm pressure on the dressing will help reduce the bleeding, and summoning assistance demonstrates good judgment.
3. The nurse should never remove a dressing when the client is potentially hemorrhaging.
4. The nurse should not leave the client alone at this time.

CLASSIFICATION

Competency Category:	Implementation
Taxonomic Level:	Application
Client Age:	Adult
Nursing Practice:	Clinical Techniques

REFERENCES

Kozier et al. (1991), p. 1308

Phipps et al. (1991), pp. 2287-2288

64 CORRECT ANSWER: 2

1. Early mental status indicators of hypokalemia include lethargy and slow performance of mental tasks.
2. Prolonged use of a thiazide diuretic enhances loss of potassium through the kidneys.
3. Smooth muscle contraction of the GI tract is depressed in hypokalemia, leading to decreased peristalsis.
4. Potassium is present in many different food types and potassium deficiency rarely occurs as a result of diet.

CLASSIFICATION

Competency Category:	Data Collection
Taxonomic Level:	Application
Client Age:	General
Nursing Practice:	Screening & Diagnosis

REFERENCES

Ignatavicius & Bayne (1991), pp. 268-274

Phipps et al. (1991), p. 768

65 CORRECT ANSWER: 3

1. Frequent voiding by itself will not reduce pain. A narcotic analgesic is required.
2. Moist heat to the flank area will not substantially decrease pain of renal calculi.
3. Administration of analgesics is correct because the pain of renal calculi is severe enough to warrant narcotic analgesia as an initial action before other comfort measures are undertaken.
4. Although ambulation will promote passage of stones, distraction is not sufficient to overcome severe pain.

CLASSIFICATION

Competency Category:	Implementation
Taxonomic Level:	Knowledge/Comprehension
Client Age:	General
Nursing Practice:	Physiological Needs

REFERENCES

Phipps et al. (1991), p. 1420

Smeltzer & Bare (1992), p. 1204

66 CORRECT ANSWER: 1

1. Cromolyn sodium (Intal) interferes with the release of histamine and is used to prevent asthma attacks.
2. Antihistamines are used to relieve allergic symptoms.
3. Cromolyn sodium (Intal) does not have an anti-inflammatory effect. Glucocorticosteroids could be used to reduce inflammation in the airways.
4. Beta-adrenergic bronchodilators relieve bronchospasms by relaxing bronchial smooth muscles. Intal does not belong to this category.

CLASSIFICATION

Competency Category:	Implementation
Taxonomic Level:	Knowledge/Comprehension
Client Age:	Child & Adolescent
Nursing Practice:	Pharmacology

REFERENCES

Foster et al. (1989), pp. 1233-1237
Whaley & Wong (1993), pp. 736-737

67 CORRECT ANSWER: 3

1. The pharmacist is responsible for dispensing medications, and not for the medication record.
2. The role of the union is to ensure that the nurse's rights are respected in the workplace. In this case, the nurse's rights are not yet called into question.
3. The nursing supervisor is the authority responsible for the safe practice of nursing care on the unit. This is the person who must be notified next of incidents of unsafe practice.
4. The nurses' professional association becomes involved in cases of unsafe practice but not at the early stages. Further investigation would be required before the nursing organization becomes involved.

CLASSIFICATION

Competency Category:	Professional Practice
Taxonomic Level:	Knowledge/Comprehension
Client Age:	General
Nursing Practice:	Professional Responsibilities

REFERENCES

Kozier et al. (1991), p. 32
Taylor et al. (1993), pp. 370, 374

68 CORRECT ANSWER: 3

1. This statement describes an intervention rather than an expected outcome.
2. This statement is client-centred, but not observable, measurable, or time-referenced.
3. This statement is client-centred, observable, measurable and time-referenced. These are the correct criteria for a well-written expected outcome.
4. This statement describes an intervention and is not measurable or time-referenced.

CLASSIFICATION

Competency Category:	Planning Care
Taxonomic Level:	Knowledge/Comprehension
Client Age:	General
Nursing Practice:	Physiological Needs

REFERENCES

Kozier et al. (1991), p. 211
Potter & Perry (1993), pp. 190-191

69 CORRECT ANSWER: 1

1. In a time of crisis, direct leadership is most appropriate. There is no time for group discussion and decision-making during a crisis, so taking control demonstrates effective leadership.
2. Limiting discussion to a specific time period describes an autocratic leader and a participative leader is preferred.
3. Facility policy determination is not the sole role or responsibility of the unit leader.
4. Allowing all staff to have their preferences may be too participative a style of leadership and one which is, at times, impossible to fulfil. It does not consider the clients, but rather the personnel.

CLASSIFICATION

Competency Category:	Collaboration & Coordination
Taxonomic Level:	Knowledge/Comprehension
Client Age:	General
Nursing Practice:	Professional Responsibilities

REFERENCES
Kozier et al. (1991), p. 30-32
Potter & Perry (1993), pp. 387-389

70 CORRECT ANSWER: 3

1. Information about her gait is important in determining the cause of her fall but is not a priority at this time.
2. Information about visual acuity is also important regarding the cause of the fall but is not a priority.
3. Level of consciousness is an important factor in assessing head injury, a potentially life-threatening condition.
4. The condition of her extremities is useful information to determine the extent of injuries but does not take the priority over a potential life-threatening condition such as head injury.

CLASSIFICATION

Competency Category:	Data Collection
Taxonomic Level:	Critical Thinking
Client Age:	Older Adult
Nursing Practice:	Screening & Diagnosis

REFERENCES
Ignatavicius & Bayne (1991), p. 928
Smeltzer & Bare (1992), p. 1733

71 CORRECT ANSWER: 4

1. A nursing diagnosis of altered nutrition is not the priority at this time and there is no evidence to suggest that this has occurred.
2. A nursing diagnosis of sleep pattern disturbance is not the priority over airway clearance.
3. A nursing diagnosis of impaired gas exchange would only be relevant if Curtis were showing signs of cyanosis, chest retractions, labored breathing, or other indications of respiratory distress.
4. A nursing diagnosis of ineffective airway clearance, a potentially life-threatening condition, is based on the related data of his cough and wheezy respirations.

CLASSIFICATION

Competency Category:	Analysis & Interpretation of Data
Taxonomic Level:	Critical Thinking
Client Age:	Child & Adolescent
Nursing Practice:	Screening & Diagnosis

REFERENCES
Castiglia & Harben (1992), pp. 544-546
Whaley & Wong (1993), pp. 726-728

72 CORRECT ANSWER: 1

1. Dyspnea and chest pain are indicative of embolism due to air infiltration or thrombus, a known complication of central venous line therapy.
2. Checking for blood return is not part of the routine management of a central line.
3. Central venous lines and their insertion sites do not require constant monitoring.
4. Flushing of a central venous line is not part of the routine management when the line is being infused continuously.

CLASSIFICATION

Competency Category:	Implementation
Taxonomic Level:	Knowledge/Comprehension
Client Age:	Older Adult
Nursing Practice:	Clinical Techniques

REFERENCES
Kozier et al. (1991), p. 1076
Smeltzer & Bare (1992), pp. 637-638

73 CORRECT ANSWER: 4

1. Waiting for the client to request an analgesic may be too late in the pain cycle for nursing interventions to be optimally effective.
2. It is not likely that the pain would have subsided later on; it is more likely that it would have increased without medication.
3. Narcotic analgesics would be necessary at this time because a bunionectomy can result in extreme pain.
4. The nurse should administer a narcotic analgesic to manage postoperative pain, especially for the first 24 hours postoperatively.

CLASSIFICATION

Competency Category:	Implementation
Taxonomic Level:	Application
Client Age:	Adult
Nursing Practice:	Pharmacology

REFERENCES
Phipps et al. (1991), p. 523
Smeltzer & Bare (1992), p. 444

74 CORRECT ANSWER: 4

1. The nurse-client trust relationship would be broken by flagging the chart, since other health care personnel have access to Jim's chart.
2. Mary is at risk and should receive counseling. However, the nurse must hold confidential all information about a client learned in the health care setting.
3. Asking to be reassigned does not address the nurse's ethical dilemma.
4. The nurse must hold confidential all information about a client learned in the health care setting. It is Jim's responsibility to inform others of his condition.

CLASSIFICATION

Competency Category:	Professional Practice
Taxonomic Level:	Affective
Client Age:	General
Nursing Practice:	Professional Responsibilities

REFERENCES

Canadian Nurses Association (1991), pp. 5-6

Flaskerud & Ungvarski (1992), p. 429

75 CORRECT ANSWER: 4

1. It is inappropriate to send a volunteer to visit Janet without first asking Janet if she would like to have such a visitor.
2. Ensuring that no one enters Janet's room is inappropriate. Janet will need support at this time and may not want to be left alone.
3. Reminding the physician to obtain Janet's permission for an autopsy of the baby may be part of the necessary post-intrauterine death procedures, but does not address the client's needs at this time.
4. Janet should be given an opportunity to express her needs. The social worker is an important resource at this time.

CLASSIFICATION

Competency Category:	Collaboration & Coordination
Taxonomic Level:	Application
Client Age:	General
Nursing Practice:	Psychosocial Needs

REFERENCES

Olds et al. (1992), pp. 754-755

Pillitteri (1992), p. 730

76 CORRECT ANSWER: 2

1. The client may be in acute pulmonary edema. Suctioning and chest physiotherapy will not improve this condition.
2. The physician must be notified when a client shows complications of left ventricular failure as this is life-threatening.
3. The semi-prone position would worsen the client's respiratory distress.
4. The client may be in acute pulmonary edema. This is a life-threatening condition that requires further action.

CLASSIFICATION

Competency Category:	Analysis & Interpretation of Data
Taxonomic Level:	Critical Thinking
Client Age:	Older Adult
Nursing Practice:	Screening & Diagnosis

REFERENCES

Black & Matassarin-Jabocs (1993), pp. 1170-1171

Phipps et al. (1991), pp. 731-732

77 CORRECT ANSWER: 2

1. The medication would be received beyond the established guideline of 30 minutes if the nurse waits until after 10 30 hours. This is of particular concern with antibiotics because serum levels may fall below the therapeutic parameter.
2. The principles of medication administration dictate that medications may be given up to 30 minutes before or after the prescribed time.
3. There would be no need to withhold the medication for a simple chest x-ray.
4. Although remembering to go to the x-ray department to administer Mr. Currie's antibiotic would ensure that he receives his medication according to the five rights, it is not the preferred choice because it would remove the nurse from the unit and other clients in the nurse's care.

CLASSIFICATION

Competency Category:	Implementation
Taxonomic Level:	Application
Client Age:	General
Nursing Practice:	Pharmacology

REFERENCES

Craven & Hirnle (1992), p. 522
Potter & Perry (1993), p. 638

78 CORRECT ANSWER: 1

1. A child with croup warrants close observation because of compromise to the airway. This action takes precedence over the other nursing actions.
2. Gastroenteritis is not as critical a diagnosis as croup.
3. The nurse has a 30-minute period of grace to administer the medication.
4. The continuous gastrostomy feeding could be delayed until after the assessment was made on the child with croup.

CLASSIFICATION

Competency Category:	Planning Care
Taxonomic Level:	Critical Thinking
Client Age:	General
Nursing Practice:	Physiological Needs

REFERENCES

Craven & Hirnle (1992), p. 136
Kozier et al. (1991), pp. 206-207

79 CORRECT ANSWER: 4

1. Drawing the curtains around the bed provides privacy, which is part of establishing rapport but not part of therapeutic communication.
2. To display caring is part of therapeutic communication, but standing will not facilitate eye-to-eye contact.
3. Building trust is part of therapeutic communication, but talking about the hockey game will not necessarily have this effect. Casual conversation is a form of social interaction rather than therapeutic communication.
4. This is the correct response as therapeutic communication involves gathering more information about the client's perceptions concerning admission and health status.

CLASSIFICATION

Competency Category:	Implementation
Taxonomic Level:	Application
Client Age:	General
Nursing Practice:	Communication

REFERENCES
Haber & McMahon (1992), p. 134
Potter & Perry (1993), pp. 319-320

80 CORRECT ANSWER: 3

1. Focusing on the number of visitors is not indicative of readiness to accept change.
2. The nurse's behavior of inconsistently informing visitors indicates lack of interest in supporting change.
3. The nurse's behavior of rescheduling nursing care demonstrates an acceptance of the change in visiting hours.
4. The nurse is using an inappropriate channel (i.e., the visitors) for expressing concerns regarding the change in visiting hours.

CLASSIFICATION

Competency Category:	Professional Practice
Taxonomic Level:	Critical Thinking
Client Age:	General
Nursing Practice:	Professional Responsibilities

REFERENCES
Kozier et al. (1991), p. 278
Taylor et al. (1993), pp. 371-373

81 CORRECT ANSWER: 1

1. Because of his chronic fatigue and his age, Mr. Cook will tire more quickly and will require periodic rest intervals.
2. The nursing assessment is the basis upon which the care plan is developed. Postponing the collection of data is therefore incorrect.
3. Although listening to Mr. Cook reminisce and talk about his family is therapeutic, it would not be a useful strategy for gathering data for the initial assessment.
4. Completing the entire assessment will be too tiring for Mr. Cook.

CLASSIFICATION

Competency Category:	Data Collection
Taxonomic Level:	Application
Client Age:	Older Adult
Nursing Practice:	Communication

REFERENCES
Beck et al. (1993), pp. 187-188
Birchenall & Streight (1993), pp. 116-117

82 CORRECT ANSWER: 4

1. Assessment provides data about the client's past and present health status but does not necessarily help to establish expected outcomes.
2. Evaluating the appropriateness of the nursing strategies is done by comparing client behaviors to expected outcomes. Therefore, this step comes later in the care plan.
3. Developing nursing diagnoses is an important part of the nursing process but does not establish expected outcomes.
4. Expected outcomes are established by identifying client behaviors that indicate the goals have been met.

CLASSIFICATION

Competency Category:	Planning Care
Taxonomic Level:	Knowledge/Comprehension
Client Age:	General
Nursing Practice:	Professional Responsibilities

REFERENCES
Kozier et al. (1991), p. 208
Potter & Perry (1993), p. 222

83 CORRECT ANSWER: 3

1. Setting up suction equipment may be required but the nurse would have to leave the client unsupervised while doing this, and this client should not be left unsupervised.
2. Restraint may cause further injury to the individual due to the strong muscle activity involved in seizures.
3. By staying with the client while waiting for help to arrive, the nurse can try to prevent injury and monitor the client.
4. The use of touch in a therapeutic manner is important, but the priority is to stay with the client and call for help.

CLASSIFICATION

Competency Category:	Evaluation
Taxonomic Level:	Application
Client Age:	General
Nursing Practice:	Physiological Needs

REFERENCES
Black & Matassarin-Jabocs (1993), p. 761
Smeltzer & Bare (1992), pp. 1723, 1728

84 CORRECT ANSWER: 3

1. An incident report should also be completed. Vital signs are not pertinent for this medication.
2. Assessing the client is appropriate; however, the nurse's accountability is not complete unless an incident report is completed.
3. The physician and nursing supervisor should be notified. Incident reports describing what happened should be completed. They are used for information that may prevent future medication errors.
4. The physician and nursing supervisor should be notified, and an incident report must also be completed. The physician will order whether or not to withhold the next dose.

CLASSIFICATION

Competency Category:	Professional Practice
Taxonomic Level:	Knowledge/Comprehension
Client Age:	General
Nursing Practice:	Pharmacology

REFERENCES

Craven & Hirnle (1992), p. 587
Potter & Perry (1993), p. 640

85 CORRECT ANSWER: 2

1. Mr. Dougherty is not consuming sufficient fluids to prevent clot formation in the urine following a TURP.
2. Pink urine that contains no clots is the expected outcome for discharge.
3. Mr. Dougherty's plan to paint his living room is unrealistic. This shows a lack of knowledge about activity restriction following TURP.
4. A client who still requires Demerol for pain relief is probably not ready for discharge.

CLASSIFICATION

Competency Category:	Evaluation
Taxonomic Level:	Application
Client Age:	Older Adult
Nursing Practice:	Screening & Diagnosis

REFERENCES

Ignatavicius & Bayne (1991), p. 1749
Smeltzer & Bare (1992), p. 1331

86 CORRECT ANSWER: 3

1. Facing the client directly is a good technique for nurses to use when working with the hearing impaired, but there is no indication that Mrs. Raven has a hearing loss.
2. Being able to see others will not necessarily remove the voices or lessen her fear. It may be frightening if no one speaks her language.
3. Asking the interpreter to explain should help to remove Mrs. Raven's fear of the unknown while orienting her to the immediate surroundings.
4. If the client does not understand where the voices are coming from, lowering the volume will not lessen her fear.

CLASSIFICATION

Competency Category:	Implementation
Taxonomic Level:	Application
Client Age:	Older Adult
Nursing Practice:	Psychosocial Needs

REFERENCES

Black & Matassarin-Jabocs (1993), p. 371
Ebersole & Hess (1990), pp. 306-311

87 CORRECT ANSWER: 1

1. Digitalis used in combination with a non-potassium-sparing loop diuretic increases the risk of digitalis toxicity of which manifestations such as muscle weakness, nausea, and anorexia are indicative.
2. Hypokalemia is probable, not hyperkalemia.
3. Lanoxin and Lasix do not interact to increase the effectiveness of the diuretic.
4. Lanoxin and Lasix do not interact to decrease the effectiveness of the diuretic.

CLASSIFICATION

Competency Category:	Implementation
Taxonomic Level:	Application
Client Age:	Older Adult
Nursing Practice:	Pharmacology

REFERENCES

Loebl et al. (1991), p. 435
Smeltzer & Bare (1992), p. 188

88 CORRECT ANSWER: 2

1. Reviewing the procedures with physicians takes the responsibility for updating current practice away from the nurse and makes the assumption that the physician is aware of current practice standards for nurses.
2. Sharing information among colleagues provides opportunities for the nurse to have any questions/concerns clarified. It is the responsibility of the entire nursing team to orient colleagues to changes in policies and procedures.
3. Attending conferences is one method of updating one's knowledge of current practice, but is neither timely nor realistic in this situation and does not address unit-specific policies.
4. It is not necessary for the nurse to participate in policy development to be updated.

CLASSIFICATION

Competency Category:	Professional Practice
Taxonomic Level:	Knowledge/Comprehension
Client Age:	General
Nursing Practice:	Professional Responsibilities

REFERENCES

Craven & Hirnle (1992), pp. 17-19
Ellis & Hartley (1992), pp. 448-449

89 CORRECT ANSWER: 2

1. There should be no need for this extent of mobility assistance.
2. There may be adequate resources currently in place for the Dubinskis, or for the nurse to build on, once assessed.
3. A nurse may already be making visits or the client may be involved in some other program.
4. This presumes that the family should take over the care, and represents an unfair responsibility to place on the family.

CLASSIFICATION

Competency Category:	Planning Care
Taxonomic Level:	Knowledge/Comprehension
Client Age:	Older Adult
Nursing Practice:	Communication

REFERENCES

Kozier et al. (1991), p. 219
Potter & Perry (1993), pp. 126-127

90 CORRECT ANSWER: 3

1. Enlarged thyroid is a side effect of lithium use and does not indicate a medication interaction.
2. Polyuria and polydipsia are common side effects of lithium and do not indicate a medication interaction.
3. Nurses should observe for changes in lithium levels (elevated levels) in concurrent use of lithium and indomethacin. Lithium poisoning has no specific antidote and toxic reactions occur with plasma levels exceeding 2 mEq/L.
4. Therapeutic plasma levels can be as low as 0.2 mEq/L in elderly clients.

CLASSIFICATION

Competency Category:	Implementation
Taxonomic Level:	Knowledge/Comprehension
Client Age:	Older Adult
Nursing Practice:	Pharmacology

REFERENCES

Beck et al. (1993), p. 494
Canadian Pharmaceutical Association (1994), p. 696

91 CORRECT ANSWER: 3

1. Offering total care may help the immediate situation for Mrs. Watson, but if the other nurse is consistently not providing good nursing care, it will not prevent a recurrence with other clients.
2. Observing the other nurse would not necessarily help Mrs. Watson, and may put other clients at risk.
3. By representing the client's view, the nurse can clarify and address the situation. It may be that other circumstances are involved.
4. The issue would not be dealt with openly and may not be identified until the next formal evaluation, if at all. Documenting the incident will not likely help Mrs. Watson.

CLASSIFICATION

Competency Category:	Professional Practice
Taxonomic Level:	Critical Thinking
Client Age:	Adult
Nursing Practice:	Professional Responsibilities

REFERENCES

Craven & Hirnle (1992), p. 278
Kozier et al. (1991), p. 28

92 CORRECT ANSWER: 4

1. The client's needs should be assessed before a plan is developed and written.
2. Evaluation of teaching would occur only after other steps of the nursing process have been completed.
3. Reviewing the preoperative checklist involves assessment but would not be the first step in planning care.
4. Assessment of client needs is the first step in planning care.

CLASSIFICATION

Competency Category:	Planning Care
Taxonomic Level:	Knowledge/Comprehension
Client Age:	General
Nursing Practice:	Communication

REFERENCES

Craven & Hirnle (1992), pp. 84-86
Potter & Perry (1993), p. 149

93 CORRECT ANSWER: 2

1. Water is the appropriate solution to flush the tube.
2. Elevating the head of the bed decreases the risk of aspiration of the feeding.
3. Auscultating the lungs is inappropriate because the gastrostomy tube goes through the abdominal wall into the stomach.
4. The feeding should be infused at room temperature.

CLASSIFICATION

Competency Category:	Implementation
Taxonomic Level:	Knowledge/Comprehension
Client Age:	General
Nursing Practice:	Clinical Techniques

REFERENCES

Kozier et al. (1991), pp. 1029-1030
Timby & Lewis (1992), pp. 144-151

94 CORRECT ANSWER: 2

1. There is no information to indicate that Mrs. Goldstein has stopped eating and is refusing her insulin because of lack of knowledge. Further assessment is required.
2. Although Mrs. Goldstein's diabetes is under control, she is not cooperating with her therapeutic regimen. It is the nurse's responsibility to assess Mrs. Goldstein for her perceptions of her illness and her readiness for discharge.
3. Arrangements may need to be made for follow-up at home, but it is premature to intervene before further assessment has been conducted.
4. Mrs. Goldstein will need to have her blood sugar monitored if she refuses to eat and take her insulin, but this option does nothing toward solving the problem of failing to cooperate with her therapeutic regimen.

CLASSIFICATION

Competency Category:	Planning Care
Taxonomic Level:	Application
Client Age:	Older Adult
Nursing Practice:	Psychosocial Needs

REFERENCES

Black & Matassarin-Jabocs (1993), p. 138
Ellis & Hartley (1992), p. 139

95 CORRECT ANSWER: 3

1. Hypernatremia is not associated with digitalis toxicity.
2. Hypochloremia is not associated with digitalis toxicity.
3. Potassium depletion (i.e., hypokalemia) predisposes the client to digitalis toxicity and is the most common electrolyte disturbance.
4. Hyponatremia is not associated with digitalis toxicity.

CLASSIFICATION

Competency Category:	Implementation
Taxonomic Level:	Knowledge/Comprehension
Client Age:	General
Nursing Practice:	Pharmacology

REFERENCES

Canadian Pharmaceutical Association (1994), p. 671
Malseed & Girton (1990), p. 283

96 CORRECT ANSWER: 2

1. Taking all doses at the same time does not indicate safe practice.
2. Making a checklist indicates that the client has mastered one aspect of safe self-medication.
3. Double-dosing after a missed dose is an unsafe practice and indicates that the client has not met the goal.
4. Information documented by the client's daughter is not a measure of the goal as the goal states that it is the client who must demonstrate the desired behavior.

CLASSIFICATION

Competency Category:	Evaluation
Taxonomic Level:	Application
Client Age:	General
Nursing Practice:	Pharmacology

REFERENCES

Kozier et al. (1991), pp. 211, 231
Taylor et al. (1993), pp. 269, 316

97 CORRECT ANSWER: 2

1. This entry is well-organized by body system; however, important information has been omitted.
2. This entry is well-organized by body system and all important information is concisely conveyed.
3. This entry includes all important information; however, it is not well-organized. Kegel exercises (perineal exercises) should be discussed with the other urinary tract information.
4. This entry includes some extraneous information and is not well-organized according to body system. Kegel exercises (perineal exercises) should be discussed along with the other urinary tract information.

CLASSIFICATION

Competency Category:	Implementation
Taxonomic Level:	Application
Client Age:	Adult
Nursing Practice:	Professional Responsibilities

REFERENCES

Kozier et al. (1991), p. 315
Smeltzer & Bare (1991), pp. 11-12

98 CORRECT ANSWER: 3

1. Peer-evaluation on a regular basis is only one component of self-evaluation.
2. Writing weaknesses and developing a plan is not wrong, but looking at strengths is also important.
3. Reflecting on performance and determining areas for growth are ways of practicing ongoing self-evaluation.
4. Meeting with the nursing supervisor represents evaluation from the nursing supervisor, not a self-evaluation.

CLASSIFICATION

Competency Category:	Professional Practice
Taxonomic Level:	Knowledge/Comprehension
Client Age:	General
Nursing Practice:	Professional Responsibilities

REFERENCES

Craven & Hirnle (1992), p. 1257
Ellis & Hartley (1992), pp. 226-231

99 CORRECT ANSWER: 1

1. The client is always the primary source of information if the client is deemed reliable.
2. Mrs. Gomez's daughter can be an important additional source of information. However, the client (i.e., Mrs. Gomez) should be the primary source of information, provided she is deemed reliable.
3. Mrs. Gomez's chart will provide information about what was prescribed, but that may not be what the client is currently taking. Also, it will not provide information from the client's perspective.
4. While it is important to use additional reliable sources of information, the nursing assessment should begin with the client's perspective.

CLASSIFICATION

Competency Category:	Data Collection
Taxonomic Level:	Knowledge/Comprehension
Client Age:	Older Adult
Nursing Practice:	Communication

REFERENCES

Carnevali & Patrick (1993), pp. 23, 27
Taylor et al. (1993), p. 231

100 CORRECT ANSWER: 4

1. Calling the physician would not be the best action because a further attempt should be made to resolve the problem with the colleague.
2. It is preferable to discuss the situation with the nurse involved before consulting other colleagues.
3. Asking the pharmacist to speak to the colleague is not the best solution to the problem because it is more confrontational than referring the colleague to a reference book.
4. Consulting a drug reference book together would validate the correct technique.

CLASSIFICATION

Competency Category:	Professional Practice
Taxonomic Level:	Critical Thinking
Client Age:	General
Nursing Practice:	Professional Responsibilities

REFERENCES

Ellis & Hartley (1992), pp. 231-232
Malseed & Girton (1990), p. 45

CASE 9

101 CORRECT ANSWER: 4

1. It is not the legal responsibility of the nurse to review the consent form with the client.
2. Informing the client about the implications of the surgery is incorrect because it is not within the scope of nursing practice.
3. Although teaching the client about the role of the prostate may be done, it does not address the issue of informed consent. Sexual activity is only one aspect of the implications of this surgery.
4. It is the nurse's responsibility to assess clients' understanding of their care, and to consult the practitioner who is legally responsible for obtaining informed consent.

CLASSIFICATION

Competency Category:	Professional Practice
Taxonomic Level:	Application
Client Age:	Older Adult
Nursing Practice:	Professional Responsibilities

REFERENCES

Baird et al. (1991), p. 470
Canadian Nurses Association (1991), pp. 3-6

102 CORRECT ANSWER: 1

1. Evaluating the client's response to medication is a standard of practice and an important part of the nursing process. It is a legal requirement within the administration of medications.
2. Observing for urinary retention is an action the nurse should take, but is not related to the administration of the preoperative medication.
3. Preoperative teaching should be completed prior to the administration of preoperative sedation.
4. Notifying the anesthetist is not required. The record in the client's chart serves as notification that the medication was administered.

CLASSIFICATION

Competency Category:	Implementation
Taxonomic Level:	Knowledge/Comprehension
Client Age:	Older Adult
Nursing Practice:	Pharmacology

REFERENCES

Craven & Hirnle (1992), p. 523
Kozier et al. (1991), p. 1266

103 CORRECT ANSWER: 2

1. Hematuria is considered normal up to 3 days following prostate surgery.
2. Checking the catheter drainage system confirms catheter patency.
3. 1000 mL is only one third of the typical fluid requirements following prostatic surgery.
4. The nursing focus is to promote emptying of the bladder to decrease pressure on the surgical site.

CLASSIFICATION

Competency Category:	Implementation
Taxonomic Level:	Application
Client Age:	Older Adult
Nursing Practice:	Clinical Techniques

REFERENCES

Black & Matassarin-Jabocs (1993), pp. 2098-2100
Phipps et al. (1991), p. 1428

104 CORRECT ANSWER: 3

1. Contacting another health worker does not represent the client in the true spirit of advocacy. This implies that the nurse has transferred the role of client advocate to another person.
2. Volunteering to be Mr. Ali's primary nurse is an unrealistic solution and does not represent advocacy because the other team members would not increase their understanding of Mr. Ali's needs.
3. Representing the client's point of view by interpreting and explaining the client's rights is the essence of responsible advocacy.
4. Although having the family present during prayer may be a nursing action that is taken, it is not a description of advocacy.

CLASSIFICATION

Competency Category: Professional Practice
Taxonomic Level: Affective
Client Age: Older Adult
Nursing Practice: Professional Responsibilities

REFERENCES

Baird et al. (1991), pp. 32-33
Kozier et al. (1991), pp. 28-29

105 CORRECT ANSWER: 2

1. Perineal exercises assist in the regaining of muscle tone and should therefore be encouraged, not discouraged.
2. Measuring volume of voidings assesses bladder tone and recovery from surgical intervention.
3. Measurement of fluid intake is not a required assessment by day 4 postoperative.
4. Should recatheterization be required, it would be done by a professional because of risk of trauma to the surgical area.

CLASSIFICATION

Competency Category: Planning Care
Taxonomic Level: Knowledge/Comprehension
Client Age: Older Adult
Nursing Practice: Clinical Techniques

REFERENCES

Black & Matassarin-Jabocs (1993), p. 2099
Ignatavicius & Bayne (1991), p. 1748

106 CORRECT ANSWER: 2

1. Discussing Mr. Ali's role within the family does not assess his perception of discharge needs.
2. Asking Mr. Ali how he sees his surgery impacting on his life opens up discussion with him about his perception of his own needs. Therefore, he is able to express what he feels is most important.
3. Exploring Mr. Ali's feelings regarding his diagnosis does not validate his needs for discharge follow-up.
4. Assessing Mr. Ali's understanding of his activity restrictions limits the validation of his perceived needs.

CLASSIFICATION

Competency Category: Implementation
Taxonomic Level: Application
Client Age: Older Adult
Nursing Practice: Communication

REFERENCES

Arnold & Boggs (1989), p. 254
Smith (1992), p. 43

CASE 10

107 CORRECT ANSWER: 3

1. With aging, the small airways close due to a decrease in elastic recoil of the lung tissue.
2. Attempting to cough while ambulating will potentiate discomfort.
3. With aging, the loss of lung tissue elasticity and ciliary action are compensated by more rapid breathing.
4. Due to a decrease in muscle elasticity with aging, the older client's lungs cannot expand to the size of those of a younger person.

CLASSIFICATION

Competency Category:	Implementation
Taxonomic Level:	Knowledge/Comprehension
Client Age:	Older Adult
Nursing Practice:	Physiological Needs

REFERENCES

Craven & Hirnle (1992), p. 752
Taylor et al. (1993), p. 192

108 CORRECT ANSWER: 2

1. The nurse should not wait for the bladder to become distended before catheterizing.
2. Only after the client has attempted to void first on her own, without success, should she be catheterized.
3. Attempts should be made to enable the client to void on her own first.
4. Emptying the bladder every 6-8 hours will not necessarily enable the client to void on her own.

CLASSIFICATION

Competency Category:	Implementation
Taxonomic Level:	Knowledge/Comprehension
Client Age:	Older Adult
Nursing Practice:	Clinical Techniques

REFERENCES

Craven & Hirnle (1992), p. 1071
Taylor et al. (1993), p. 890

109 CORRECT ANSWER: 3

1. Age is not a factor in calculating the dosage.
2. Weight is not usually a factor in medication calculations for adults.
3. The nurse must first assess the client's degree of pain before calculating the amount of the dosage.
4. While the full p.r.n. dosage is prescribed, the nurse must first determine the degree of pain and then calculate the dosage accordingly.

CLASSIFICATION

Competency Category:	Implementation
Taxonomic Level:	Critical Thinking
Client Age:	Older Adult
Nursing Practice:	Pharmacology

REFERENCES

Smeltzer & Bare (1992), p. 85
Spencer et al. (1993), pp. 291, 295

110 CORRECT ANSWER: 4

1. Information about footwear and mobility aids are important safety issues, but not essential to mobilization care.
2. While specifying the side of the bed to get out on may reduce possible discomfort to the client, it is not essential to mobilization.
3. Frequency and length of time are not critical to the ability to mobilize.
4. It is essential that information concerning weight-bearing limitations be included to minimize the danger of dislodging/breaking the fixation device.

CLASSIFICATION

Competency Category:	Planning Care
Taxonomic Level:	Application
Client Age:	Older Adult
Nursing Practice:	Physiological Needs

REFERENCES

Black & Matassarin-Jabocs (1993), p. 1926
Smeltzer & Bare (1992), p. 1807

111 CORRECT ANSWER: 3

1. The nurse should continue to remove stool from the rectum until stool can no longer be felt with the fingertip.
2. Stool should be broken into small portions for easy removal from the rectum.
3. Feces should be removed gently as stimulation of the vagus nerve may slow the client's heart. This may not always be avoidable with this procedure, but the nurse must always be gentle.
4. The client should not hold her breath, but should instead take several cleansing breaths to relax the bowel muscle walls. Holding her breath would potentiate the valsalva maneuver.

CLASSIFICATION

Competency Category:	Implementation
Taxonomic Level:	Knowledge/Comprehension
Client Age:	Older Adult
Nursing Practice:	Clinical Techniques

REFERENCES

Craven & Hirnle (1992), p. 1123
Kozier et al. (1991), p. 1160

112 CORRECT ANSWER: 1

1. In order to sustain Mrs. Edwards' control of the planning, she should be involved in all decisions regarding her discharge.
2. Family support is important, but may reduce Mrs. Edwards' sense of control. This does not ensure proper follow-up.
3. Completing all the arrangements for Mrs. Edwards reduces her sense of control of the situation.
4. While the names and telephone numbers are helpful, it is presumptuous to assume Mrs. Edwards is able to make all the arrangements herself.

CLASSIFICATION

Competency Category:	Professional Practice
Taxonomic Level:	Application
Client Age:	Older Adult
Nursing Practice:	Professional Responsibilities

REFERENCES

Burke & Walsh (1992), p. 465
McClosky & Grace (1990), p. 182

CASE 11

113 CORRECT ANSWER: 3

1. There are no data provided to indicate that the client has a hearing loss.
2. There are no data provided which describe anxiety.
3. A language barrier is the only conclusion that can be validated with the information provided in the case, as it is specified that this client speaks only a few words of English.
4. There are no data to validate the conclusion that the client does not want to be interviewed.

CLASSIFICATION

Competency Category:	Implementation
Taxonomic Level:	Knowledge/Comprehension
Client Age:	Older Adult
Nursing Practice:	Communication

REFERENCES

Kozier et al. (1991), p. 257
Taylor et al. (1993), p. 340

114 CORRECT ANSWER: 4

1. All medications must first be verified against the original order before proceeding to the medication record.
2. The order contains all the correct information required for the safe administration of this medication and therefore does not require further clarification by the physician.
3. There is no indication for crushing the tablet in this situation.
4. The medication must be verified against the original order before administration.

CLASSIFICATION

Competency Category:	Implementation
Taxonomic Level:	Knowledge/Comprehension
Client Age:	Older Adult
Nursing Practice:	Pharmacology

REFERENCES

Kozier et al. (1991), pp. 1265, 1358
Taylor et al. (1993), p. 1195

115 CORRECT ANSWER: 4

1. Asking the client to identify herself is an acceptable method of identification if the client does not have an identification bracelet. In this client's case, there is a language barrier which might make this action less effective than checking the identification band.
2. Checking any identification that is not on the client's person is not a safe way to identify the client. For example, there may be another client or even a visitor occupying the bed instead of the client.
3. Asking the client a closed question such as "Are you Mrs. Huang?" could lead to errors in identification if the client answers "Yes" in error.
4. Checking the identification band is universally accepted as the safest and most effective method of identifying the client before administering a medication.

CLASSIFICATION

Competency Category:	Implementation
Taxonomic Level:	Knowledge/Comprehension
Client Age:	Older Adult
Nursing Practice:	Pharmacology

REFERENCES
Kozier et al. (1991), p. 1265
Taylor et al. (1993), p. 1203

116 CORRECT ANSWER: 1

1. Demonstration is the most appropriate technique to use with the client whose understanding of English is minimal. This intervention also reinforces teaching of the exercises so that it can be performed correctly by the client.
2. Written instructions for the client who has a minimal knowledge of English are not appropriate as she may not be able to understand the instructions.
3. Pointing to the incentive spirometer assumes that the client already knows what to do with it, and this may not be the case.
4. Asking the client to perform the exercises assumes that she understands the request and that she remembers the preoperative teaching sufficiently well to perform the exercises independently.

CLASSIFICATION

Competency Category:	Implementation
Taxonomic Level:	Application
Client Age:	Older Adult
Nursing Practice:	Communication

REFERENCES
Phipps et al. (1991), p. 505
Smeltzer & Bare (1992) p. 64

117 CORRECT ANSWER: 2

1. Discontinuing the I.V. is dependent on the physiological assessment of the client status, and not on an external event such as return to the unit.
2. The ability to tolerate oral fluids is the recognized sign of the client's readiness to have the I.V. discontinued.
3. Wound drainage is not a reliable indicator of the appropriateness of I.V. discontinuation. Many clients do not have any drainage at all after surgery but still require their I.V. infusion.
4. Using a time factor as the basis for decision-making is incorrect as the nurse must assess the client's physiological status.

CLASSIFICATION

Competency Category:	Implementation
Taxonomic Level:	Knowledge/Comprehension
Client Age:	Older Adult
Nursing Practice:	Clinical Techniques

REFERENCES

Phipps et al. (1991), pp. 518-519
Smeltzer & Bare (1992), p. 446

118 CORRECT ANSWER: 2

1. While a glossary is a good intervention to assist clients who do not speak the dominant language, it does not address the learning need identified by the nurse in the situation; i.e., to enhance nursing care of culturally different clients in the future.
2. Exploring the literature is the best way for the nurse to meet knowledge requirements in an unfamiliar area. Furthermore, expanding the inquiry beyond just this client's cultural group is an effective way for the nurse to become prepared to respond to the needs of clients from various cultural backgrounds.
3. If the nurse uses present knowledge in future situations of a similar nature, it is possible that the same errors may be repeated. The identified need in this situation is to enhance nursing care in the future.
4. A standard care plan is not an appropriate solution as it assumes that all clients from Mrs. Huang's cultural group have the same needs as Mrs. Huang and may promote cultural stereotypes.

CLASSIFICATION

Competency Category:	Professional Practice
Taxonomic Level:	Affective
Client Age:	Older Adult
Nursing Practice:	Professional Responsibilities

REFERENCES

Kozier et al. (1991), pp. 24-25
Taylor et al. (1993), pp. 120-124

INDEPENDENT ITEMS

119 CORRECT ANSWER: 3

1. Pulse decreases initially with increased intracranial pressure.
2. Body temperature does not decrease with increased intracranial pressure.
3. An increase in his systolic blood pressure would indicate that Mr. Howard is showing signs of increased intracranial pressure.
4. Withdrawing his legs in response to a pinprick measures his level of consciousness and may indicate an improvement and not necessarily a deterioration in his condition.

CLASSIFICATION

Competency Category:	Evaluation
Taxonomic Level:	Application
Client Age:	General
Nursing Practice:	Screening & Diagnosis

REFERENCES

Lewis & Collier (1992), p. 1525
Smeltzer & Bare (1992), p. 1733

120 CORRECT ANSWER: 1

1. It is unrealistic to expect one nurse to simultaneously assess q. 15 minute vital signs and administer stat. medications to two acutely ill clients, as well as administer insulin to a third client. This represents an urgent situation that requires reassignment.
2. This is a workload issue, not a nursing knowledge issue.
3. Reprioritizing will not lead to the attainment of the therapeutic goals of the clients described in the situation.
4. Administering the insulin indicates poor priority-setting as the acutely ill clients will be neglected while this is being done.

CLASSIFICATION

Competency Category:	Professional Practice
Taxonomic Level:	Critical Thinking
Client Age:	General
Nursing Practice:	Professional Responsibilities

REFERENCES

Baumgart (1992), p. 234
Ellis & Hartley (1992), pp. 398-399, 418-419

121 CORRECT ANSWER: 1

1. With sustained use of anti-inflammatory medications, medications should be given with, or following food, to minimize gastric irritation. The shower should precede physiotherapy to reduce stiffness and pain.
2. Anti-inflammatory medications can cause gastric irritation and should be given with food. The shower should precede physiotherapy.
3. The shower and medications should precede the physiotherapy session as the client is likely to be more comfortable and less stiff.
4. The medications should be taken prior to the physiotherapy session to reduce stiffness.

CLASSIFICATION

Competency Category:	Planning Care
Taxonomic Level:	Application
Client Age:	Adult
Nursing Practice:	Physiological Needs

REFERENCES

Ignatavicius & Bayne (1991), pp. 697-699

Phipps et al. (1991), pp. 2062-2065

122 CORRECT ANSWER: 3

1. Mrs. Thornton requires orientation to her new environment before she is allowed to ambulate independently.
2. Bed rest and side rails are unnecessary for an individual who is able to function independently. Sitting with the client does not alleviate these restrictions.
3. An analysis of the data should lead the nurse to remove the unnecessary restrictions to minimize the client's distress.
4. There is no reason to maintain the client in bed. Explaining to the client the reason for the restrictions does nothing to remove the restrictions, or decrease the client's distress.

CLASSIFICATION

Competency Category:	Evaluation
Taxonomic Level:	Application
Client Age:	Adult
Nursing Practice:	Physiological Needs

REFERENCES

Craven & Hirnle (1992), p. 1201

Potter & Perry (1993), p. 1557

123 CORRECT ANSWER: 3

1. Preparing equipment for a forceps delivery does not address Mrs. Chan's concerns, and does not represent the nurse as a client advocate.
2. Although exploring client needs is evidence of client advocacy, it would be inappropriate to discuss at this time.
3. Negotiating for unassisted delivery demonstrates client advocacy as it addresses Mrs. Chan's individualized request. As fetal descent is evident, there is no emergent need for assisted delivery.
4. Having Mrs. Chan reiterate her wishes is not an attempt at client advocacy. It puts the responsibility for advocacy on the client at an inappropriate time.

CLASSIFICATION

Competency Category:	Professional Practice
Taxonomic Level:	Application
Client Age:	Adult
Nursing Practice:	Professional Responsibilities

REFERENCES

Arnold & Boggs (1989), pp. 385-386
Olds et al. (1992), p. 7

124 CORRECT ANSWER: 1

1. Maintaining eye contact demonstrates that the nurse is interested in and listening to what the client says. Listening involves verbal and nonverbal communication.
2. Sitting with arms crossed portrays a defensive attitude and conveys that the nurse is protecting personal space.
3. Recording the information while the client is talking will not provide a relaxed atmosphere.
4. The nurse must allow time to reflect on and understand what the client is saying, verbally and nonverbally.

CLASSIFICATION

Competency Category:	Data Collection
Taxonomic Level:	Knowledge/Comprehension
Client Age:	General
Nursing Practice:	Communication

REFERENCES

Kozier et al. (1991), pp. 258-259
Potter & Perry (1993), p. 320

125 CORRECT ANSWER: 1

1. The nurse is justified in providing the p.r.n. medication by the physiological and behavioral responses. The child is probably denying pain because pain relief involves injection, which can be frightening.
2. Benjamin is exhibiting signs of pain. Sitting with him may be helpful, but the initial nursing action should be to alleviate his discomfort.
3. Benjamin's mother could assist in the assessment of Benjamin's pain, but there is nothing to suggest that she will be available. Benjamin might be kept in great pain for an extended period.
4. Reminding Benjamin of the importance of reporting his discomfort dismisses the real problem, which is that he probably fears the injection.

CLASSIFICATION

Competency Category:	Implementation
Taxonomic Level:	Application
Client Age:	Child & Adolescent
Nursing Practice:	Physiological Needs

REFERENCES

Kozier et al. (1991), pp. 1260-1266
Whaley & Wong (1993), pp. 593-596

126 CORRECT ANSWER: 1

1. Taking vital signs is the basic tool to assess the client.
2. Completing the nursing admission would be tiring for the client and is not a priority at this time.
3. Previous medical history is not a priority when the client is in acute respiratory distress.
4. The respiratory technologist will not provide the required data at this time.

CLASSIFICATION

Competency Category:	Data Collection
Client Age:	Older Adult
Taxonomic Level:	Knowledge/Comprehension
Nursing Practice:	Screening & Diagnosis

REFERENCES

Craven & Hirnle (1992), pp. 348-377
Kozier et al. (1991), pp. 321-354

127 CORRECT ANSWER: 1

1. Assessment of neurological and vital signs is an essential nursing intervention to perform before the client is moved.
2. Alternatives for restraints should be used. Restraining a client who has a possible head injury may exacerbate the injury.
3. The priority for this client is assessment before comfort.
4. Documentation of an incident such as a fall is a necessary nursing action, but is not the most critical part of the client's care.

CLASSIFICATION

Competency Category:	Implementation
Taxonomic Level:	Application
Client Age:	Older Adult
Nursing Practice:	Physiological Needs

REFERENCES

Eliopoulos (1993), pp. 124-125
Harkness & Dincher (1992), pp. 647-648

128 CORRECT ANSWER: 3

1. Once there is a suspicion of physical abuse, the government agency responsible for child protection must be contacted. They would then contact the police if required.
2. At this time, it would not be necessary to have Nancy's father leave. Observations of family interactions are very important when determining child abuse.
3. As a member of the health care team, it is important for the nurse to validate the interpretation of data. The identification of child abuse may require the knowledge and skills of a variety of health and social service professionals.
4. The nurse would require more data before requesting that the child's mother come to the emergency department.

CLASSIFICATION

Competency Category:	Analysis & Interpretation of Data
Taxonomic Level:	Application
Client Age:	Child & Adolescent
Nursing Practice:	Physiological Needs

REFERENCES
Foster et al. (1989), pp. 1084-1090
Whaley & Wong (1993), pp. 12, 405-417

129 CORRECT ANSWER: 2

1. Referring the client discounts the fact that Mrs. Martin may be very capable of changing her own dressing.
2. The best evidence of Mrs. Martin's self-care ability is for her to successfully demonstrate the dressing change to the nurse.
3. Giving a list of resources is part of a general discharge plan but does not relate specifically to Mrs. Martin's dressing change management.
4. Providing a video would be valuable before Mrs. Martin demonstrates a dressing change but does not show her ability for self-care of the dressing.

CLASSIFICATION

Competency Category:	Implementation
Taxonomic Level:	Application
Client Age:	Older Adult
Nursing Practice:	Communication

REFERENCES
Phipps et al. (1991), pp. 2251-2253
Potter & Perry (1993), pp. 135-137

BOOK

2

Rationales

CASE 12

1 CORRECT ANSWER: 1

1. High-Fowler's position reduces the workload on the heart and decreases venous return.
2. A physician's order would be required for the Venturi mask and for a flow rate of 8 L/min.
3. Preparing for an I.V. infusion would be correct later on, but is not appropriate as the initial action by the nurse.
4. Arranging for blood gases would not give immediate relief; a physician's order would be required for treatment based on the analysis.

CLASSIFICATION

Competency Category:	Implementation
Taxonomic Level:	Application
Client Age:	Older Adult
Nursing Practice:	Clinical Techniques

REFERENCES:

Ignatavicius & Bayne (1991), p. 2168
Smeltzer & Bare (1992), p. 696

2 CORRECT ANSWER: 3

1. Synthetics contribute more than natural fibres to the build-up of static electricity, which is dangerous given the flammability of oxygen.
2. Properly grounded equipment, with no frayed cords, is safe to use.
3. To ensure that the equipment is operating safely (e.g., the correct amount of oxygen), the ports on the mask must be checked.
4. There is no evidence that oil-based creams pose a safety risk to clients receiving oxygen therapy.

CLASSIFICATION

Competency Category:	Implementation
Taxonomic Level:	Knowledge/Comprehension
Client Age:	Older Adult
Nursing Practice:	Physiological Needs

REFERENCES

Craven & Hirnle (1992), p. 774
Taylor et al. (1993), p. 968

3 CORRECT ANSWER: 1

1. Heart rate will be affected by the medication and needs to be monitored and recorded so adjustments in dosage can be made.
2. Blood pressure is not the primary characteristic that should be recorded with this medication.
3. Respiratory rate is not affected by this medication.
4. While activity level would alter the pulse rate, it is not a characteristic that needs to be recorded.

CLASSIFICATION

Competency Category:	Implementation
Taxonomic Level:	Knowledge/Comprehension
Client Age:	Older Adult
Nursing Practice:	Pharmacology

REFERENCES

Shannon & Wilson (1992), p. 147
Ignatavicius & Bayne (1991), p. 2159

4 CORRECT ANSWER: 4

1. Checking the intravenous rate on a regular basis can be done without disturbing the client.
2. Visits by familiar individuals contribute to orientation and meaningful sensory input.
3. Muted light would be more likely to cause sensory deprivation, rather than overload, in the elderly.
4. Unfamiliar, repetitious sound can contribute to sensory overload.

CLASSIFICATION

Competency Category:	Implementation
Taxonomic Level:	Application
Client Age:	Older Adult
Nursing Practice:	Physiological Needs

REFERENCES
Black & Matassarin-Jabocs (1993), p. 371
Ignatavicius & Bayne (1991), pp. 148-150

5 CORRECT ANSWER: 2

1. Weight stability demonstrates an anticipated response to therapy and is not of particular importance to report.
2. Dizziness implies a need for close monitoring to ensure the client's safety.
3. Needing reminders would not be unexpected; this is not necessary to report.
4. Sleeping for short periods at regular intervals indicates an improvement in sleep pattern over his admission status.

CLASSIFICATION

Competency Category:	Collaboration & Coordination
Taxonomic Level:	Critical Thinking
Client Age:	Older Adult
Nursing Practice:	Professional Responsibilities

REFERENCES
Ignatavicius & Bayne (1991), p. 2166
Smeltzer & Bare (1992), p. 692

6 CORRECT ANSWER: 2

1. The length of shift remaining is immaterial if the nurse cannot manage the care alone.
2. The needs of other clients and Mr. Juliano's worsening condition take priority.
3. Administrative tasks do not take priority over the nursing care needs of the clients.
4. No matter how experienced, the practical nurse/nursing assistant cannot carry out the full range of nursing responsibilities.

CLASSIFICATION

Competency Category:	Professional Practice
Taxonomic Level:	Critical Thinking
Client Age:	Older Adult
Nursing Practice:	Professional Responsibilities

REFERENCES
Ignatavicius & Bayne (1991), p. 104
McClosky & Grace (1990), p. 492

CASE 13

7 CORRECT ANSWER: 2

1. There is no indication that the client is anxious.
2. The client's condition reflects altered nutrition because she is described as frail and anorexic.
3. Diarrhea is a common complication of tube feedings. Constipation is unlikely.
4. There is no indication that the client has a fluid volume deficit.

CLASSIFICATION

Competency Category:	Analysis & Interpretation of Data
Taxonomic Level:	Application
Client Age:	Older Adult
Nursing Practice:	Screening & Diagnosis

REFERENCES
Beare & Myers (1990), p. 355
Potter & Perry (1993), pp. 1115-1116

8 CORRECT ANSWER: 1

1. Checking for placement determines whether the tube is in the stomach before feeding.
2. The client should be placed in a right lateral position or Fowler's position to facilitate movement of the feeding from the stomach into the small intestine.
3. Changing the tubing is not necessary before each feeding.
4. Water is instilled after feeding to maintain patency; instilling before ascertaining placement of the tube may introduce water to the lungs.

CLASSIFICATION

Competency Category:	Implementation
Taxonomic Level:	Knowledge/Comprehension
Client Age:	Older Adult
Nursing Practice:	Clinical Techniques

REFERENCES
Kozier et al. (1991), p. 1017
Smeltzer & Bare (1992), pp. 448-449

9 CORRECT ANSWER: 4

1. The activity room may provide too much stimulation, given the client's current health status.
2. Removing family photos will decrease sensory stimulation and the opportunity for conversation.
3. Clocks and calendars promote orientation, but are not the most effective means of promoting sensory stimulation.
4. Talking with the client encourages use of her senses.

CLASSIFICATION

Competency Category:	Implementation
Taxonomic Level:	Application
Client Age:	Older Adult
Nursing Practice:	Physiological Needs

REFERENCES
Ebersole & Hess (1990), p. 305
Potter & Perry (1993), p. 1565

10 CORRECT ANSWER: 1

1. The nurse should assess the client's orientation status first in order to determine the cause of the confusion.
2. Sedation may increase confusion in the elderly client. There is no indication for sedation at this time.
3. Encouraging the client to express her concerns may be a subsequent intervention.
4. Encouraging the client to participate in the plan of care is not appropriate given her confused state.

CLASSIFICATION

Competency Category:	Evaluation
Taxonomic Level:	Application
Client Age:	Older Adult
Nursing Practice:	Professional Responsibilities

REFERENCES

Beare & Myers (1990), p. 387
Smeltzer & Bare (1992), p. 1841

11 CORRECT ANSWER: 3

1. Maintaining high-quality care at all times does not address the nurse's frustration.
2. Decreasing the amount of time spent with the client does not solve the problem of frustration for the nurse and may not be beneficial to the client.
3. Discussing the subject with another nurse might allow the nurse caring for the client to gain deeper insight into her feelings and to identify further steps to be taken. The nurse is requesting support.
4. This approach would not promote good communication among staff who may not be aware of the problem. This does not foster the nurse's professional growth.

CLASSIFICATION

Competency Category:	Professional Practice
Taxonomic Level:	Application
Client Age:	Older Adult
Nursing Practice:	Professional Responsibilities

REFERENCES

Canadian Nurses Association (1991), pp. 9-10
Smith (1992), pp. 174-177

12 CORRECT ANSWER: 3

1. Suctioning the oral cavity first would not clear the main air passage and may spread microorganisms.
2. Suctioning is necessary to clear the air passage; however, prolonged suctioning will decrease oxygen supply.
3. Insertion without applying suction prevents trauma to the mucous membrane.
4. The client should be placed in semi-Fowler's position as there is no indication that she is unconscious.

CLASSIFICATION

Competency Category:	Implementation
Taxonomic Level:	Knowledge/Comprehension
Client Age:	Older Adult
Nursing Practice:	Clinical Techniques

REFERENCES

Kozier et al. (1991), p. 1116
Potter & Perry (1993), pp. 1255-1259

CASE 14

13 CORRECT ANSWER: 2

1. This response may not be an accurate representation of Kyle's feelings.
2. The nurse is attempting to identify Kyle's feelings and attitudes which are the barrier to his ability to communicate.
3. By returning later, the nurse avoids the issue of Kyle's communication problem.
4. The nurse is being defensive; this will likely result in an increase in the communication barrier.

CLASSIFICATION

Competency Category: Implementation
Taxonomic Level: Application
Client Age: Child & Adolescent
Nursing Practice: Communication

REFERENCES

Kozier et al. (1991), pp. 253-254
Wilson & Kneisl (1992), pp. 846-847

14 CORRECT ANSWER: 1

1. Refraining from discussing Kyle's care with David ensures Kyle's right to confidentiality.
2. It is not necessary to refrain from caring for a client simply because the nurse may have access to personal knowledge about the client. Confidentiality is not breached by providing care.
3. The nurse should not discuss a client with anyone who is not on the health care team.
4. The principal is not a member of the health care team and should not be provided with information on Kyle's progress.

CLASSIFICATION

Competency Category: Professional Practice
Taxonomic Level: Affective
Client Age: Child & Adolescent
Nursing Practice: Professional Responsibilities

REFERENCES

Kozier et al. (1991), p. 135
Wilson & Kneisl (1992), pp. 846-848

15 CORRECT ANSWER: 1

1. Encouraging Kyle to verbalize his reasons for refusing to attend group therapy is the first step in assessing the problem of noncompliance.
2. Informing Kyle of the need to attend group therapy does not address the reason for his noncompliance.
3. Discussing Kyle's refusal with his mother and soliciting her help to encourage him to attend does not attempt to determine why Kyle is refusing to attend group therapy.
4. Telling Kyle that there is an activity that he would probably enjoy is a form of manipulation.

CLASSIFICATION

Competency Category: Professional Practice
Taxonomic Level: Affective
Client Age: Child & Adolescent
Nursing Practice: Communication

REFERENCES

Haber & McMahon (1992), p. 66
Kozier et al. (1991), p. 113

16 CORRECT ANSWER: 1

1. The nurse has accepted constructive feedback, conducted further assessment, and incorporated the colleagues' suggestion, if applicable, into the plan of care.
2. The nurse is listening but is ignoring potentially valuable input from colleagues.
3. Seeking out learning opportunities is an overreaction to constructive feedback. There was no information to suggest that the nurse was lacking in psychiatric nursing skills.
4. Lack of resources is not necessarily a reason for not being involved in the plan of care.

CLASSIFICATION

Competency Category: Professional Practice
Taxonomic Level: Affective
Client Age: Child & Adolescent
Nursing Practice: Professional Responsibilities

REFERENCES

Ellis & Hartley (1992), p. 289
Kozier et al. (1991), p. 26

17 CORRECT ANSWER: 4

1. An agency survey may not address the specific needs of Kyle and his mother and, therefore, is not a good measure of their satisfaction with nursing care.
2. Discussing their satisfaction with the individual nurses at the agency is inappropriate since it is nursing care that should be evaluated, and not the individual nurses.
3. Evidence of suicidal ideation is only one aspect of Kyle's progress and is not necessarily a measurement of client/family satisfaction.
4. If all mutually agreed upon goals have been met, it is an indication that Kyle and his mother are satisfied with the nursing care provided.

CLASSIFICATION

Competency Category: Evaluation
Taxonomic Level: Critical Thinking
Client Age: Child & Adolescent
Nursing Practice: Professional Responsibilities

REFERENCES

Christensen & Kockrow (1991), pp. 53-54
Wilson & Kneisl (1992), pp. 834-836

18 CORRECT ANSWER: 3

1. Assuring Kyle of the other nurses' qualifications does not coordinate the care plan to be implemented by other members of the nursing staff.
2. Admission as an inpatient would only be indicated if Kyle's condition deteriorated, and not because the nurse was not available.
3. By discussing the treatment plan, coordination of the care plan has occurred with other members of the nursing staff as well as with Kyle and his mother.
4. The nurse is validating that Kyle and his mother will be able to follow through on the treatment plan, but no provision has been made for continuity of care with other members of the nursing staff.

CLASSIFICATION

Competency Category:	Collaboration & Coordination
Taxonomic Level:	Application
Client Age:	Child & Adolescent
Nursing Practice:	Professional Responsibilities

REFERENCES

Christensen & Kockrow (1991), p. 52
Wilson & Kneisl (1992), p. 424

CASE 15

19 CORRECT ANSWER: 2

1. Post-test counseling would promote psychological well-being in the initial phase of the illness but is not a consideration at this stage of the disease.
2. In the late phase of AIDS, central nervous system disease may cause memory loss and mood changes that can result in depression and anger.
3. Blood and body fluid precautions are universally used. Because of this, the threat to the client's psychological well-being should not be overwhelming.
4. Policies dealing with documentation would have a direct impact on the health care team, not the client.

CLASSIFICATION

Competency Category:	Analysis & Interpretation of Data
Taxonomic Level:	Knowledge/Comprehension
Client Age:	Adult
Nursing Practice:	Psychosocial Needs

REFERENCES

Durham & Cohen (1991), pp. 124-125
Flaskerud & Ungvarski (1992), pp. 250-251

20 CORRECT ANSWER: 3

1. Referral to a sex therapist would be premature without first assessing the partner's concerns.
2. The nurse should not assume that teaching is required before assessing the partner's concerns.
3. The partner's concerns would be important to discuss in order to assess sexual health and knowledge.
4. Although a sexual history may be relevant to Mr. Collier's partner's concerns, it would be premature without first determining the nature of the concerns.

CLASSIFICATION

Competency Category:	Implementation
Taxonomic Level:	Affective
Client Age:	Adult
Nursing Practice:	Communication

REFERENCES

Fogel & Lauver (1990), p. 24
Potter & Perry (1993), pp. 962-963

21 CORRECT ANSWER: 2

1. Hot beverages will aggravate the painful swallowing associated with AIDS.
2. Spicy, acidic, or salty drinks should be avoided as they aggravate dysphagia and painful swallowing which are common manifestations in terminal AIDS.
3. Making Mr. Collier responsible for documentation is not appropriate for his present condition and terminal illness.
4. At Mr. Collier's terminal stage of illness, total parenteral nutrition would not be indicated.

CLASSIFICATION

Competency Category:	Implementation
Taxonomic Level:	Application
Client Age:	Adult
Nursing Practice:	Physiological Needs

REFERENCES

Durham & Cohen (1991), p. 217
Flaskerud & Ungvarski (1992), p. 165

22 CORRECT ANSWER: 2

1. A foot board would be used to prevent footdrop. This is not a high priority with Mr. Collier it is more important to support all his limbs.
2. With tumor invasion and opportunistic infections, arthralgia and myalgias will occur. Supporting the limbs will minimize localized bone, nerve, and visceral pain.
3. Maintaining alignment of the whole body during turning is not necessary for the client since spinal injury is not present. This measure is not used to promote comfort.
4. Due to the fatigue and generalized arthralgia associated with terminal AIDS, an overhead trapeze would only increase Mr. Collier's pain.

CLASSIFICATION

Competency Category:	Implementation
Taxonomic Level:	Application
Client Age:	Adult
Nursing Practice:	Clinical Techniques

REFERENCES

Durham & Cohen (1991), p. 219
Phipps et al. (1991), p. 228

23 CORRECT ANSWER: 3

1. Since the client is in a respite care facility, Mr. Collier's partner need not be responsible for transferring him.
2. Isometric exercises would be indicated for maintaining strength and endurance training. In Mr. Lewis's case, this is not the priority.
3. Range-of-motion exercises would maintain the client's functional ability.
4. In the terminal stage of his illness, retraining would not be appropriate.

CLASSIFICATION

Competency Category:	Implementation
Taxonomic Level:	Application
Client Age:	Adult
Nursing Practice:	Physiological Needs

REFERENCES

Durham & Cohen (1991), p. 289
Flaskerud & Ungvarski (1992), p. 171

24 CORRECT ANSWER: 2

1. When the client refuses to consent, the nurse is obliged to clarify the client's understanding.
2. Nurses have an obligation to value autonomy in clients. Respecting the client's right to refuse would help him maintain self-direction and allow him to make choices within his capabilities.
3. Coercion or subtle manipulation would nullify the voluntary aspect of the client's consent.
4. Prior to notifying the physician, the nurse should assess the client's understanding and reasons for refusing.

CLASSIFICATION

Competency Category:	Professional Practice
Taxonomic Level:	Affective
Client Age:	Adult
Nursing Practice:	Pharmacology

REFERENCES

Canadian Nurses Association (1991), p. 3
Taylor et al. (1993), p. 81

CASE 16

25 CORRECT ANSWER: 1

1. Determining if Jane's parents respond immediately to infant cries assesses their facilitation of the development of trust in the infant.
2. Asking about the use of a pacifier determines if the parents are meeting the baby's comfort needs, and would not necessarily facilitate the development of trust in the infant.
3. Asking about Jane's feeding pattern would be more important than the types of food when determining the development of trust.
4. Asking about the types of toys provided would assess how the parents view the baby's cognitive levels rather than the level of trust.

CLASSIFICATION

Competency Category:	Data Collection
Taxonomic Level:	Critical Thinking
Client Age:	Child & Adolescent
Nursing Practice:	Communication

REFERENCES

Jackson & Saunders (1993), pp. 251-252
Whaley & Wong (1993), pp. 274-275

26 CORRECT ANSWER: 1

1. Decreased urinary output, sunken fontanels, and decreased skin turgor are common symptoms of dehydration in the infant.
2. With hypervolemia, urinary output would increase, not decrease.
3. Although hyponatremia is a component of dehydration syndrome, the nurse's assessment data do not include serum electrolyte results.
4. In water intoxication, urinary output increases and vomiting and diarrhea occur.

CLASSIFICATION

Competency Category:	Analysis & Interpretation of Data
Taxonomic Level:	Knowledge/Comprehension
Client Age:	Child & Adolescent
Nursing Practice:	Screening & Diagnosis

REFERENCES

Jackson & Saunders (1993), pp. 605-612

Whaley & Wong (1993), pp. 759-762

27 CORRECT ANSWER: 1

1. Elevating the crib sides fully at all times prevents the child from rolling out and also prevents other children from climbing into Jane's crib.
2. For safety reasons, infant mobiles must hang at least 30 cm above the face so that the infant cannot become entangled in them.
3. A bubble top is unnecessary for a 3-month-old child, but is used with toddlers who are able to climb.
4. It is unsafe to have a pillow in the crib as it could smother the child.

CLASSIFICATION

Competency Category:	Implementation
Taxonomic Level:	Application
Client Age:	Child & Adolescent
Nursing Practice:	Physiological Needs

REFERENCES

Castiglia & Harben (1992), pp. 246, 370

Whaley & Wong (1993), pp. 300, 303

28 CORRECT ANSWER: 1

1. The parents need to be assisted and to have hands-on experience in bathing Jane several times in order to feel comfortable.
2. Ensuring that staff bathe the baby would not help the parents overcome their fears.
3. Having follow-up supervision at home would indicate a lack of trust in the parents' ability to bathe Jane.
4. Having the parents demonstrate their bathing technique is part of assessment, and not an intervention that promotes hygiene.

CLASSIFICATION

Competency Category:	Implementation
Taxonomic Level:	Application
Client Age:	Child & Adolescent
Nursing Practice:	Physiological Needs

REFERENCES

Castiglia & Harben (1992), p. 140

Whaley & Wong (1993), pp. 651-652

29 CORRECT ANSWER: 1

1. **Caring includes giving help to parents when they appear less able to cope with child care activities such as feeding.**
2. The nurse should not place the responsibility of contacting the social worker on the parents.
3. Visiting time should be determined by the parents. The nurse should consider the parents' level of fatigue.
4. Offering the parents general reading material on parenting skills is not the best way of demonstrating a caring attitude.

CLASSIFICATION

Competency Category:	Professional Practice
Taxonomic Level:	Critical Thinking
Client Age:	Child & Adolescent
Nursing Practice:	Psychosocial Needs

REFERENCES
Haber & McMahon (1992), p. 269
Whaley & Wong (1993), pp. 330-332

CASE 17

30 CORRECT ANSWER: 2

1. Religious affiliation and marital status have little influence on menopause.
2. **In cultures where attitudes toward aging are positive, menopause is less stressful. In cultures that value youth and reproductivity, menopause may be stressful. A woman's expectations/ feelings strongly influence her emotional state during menopause.**
3. Her financial status has no bearing on menopause. Her husband's attitude toward her could have a positive or negative influence.
4. Socioeconomic status does not influence menopause. The number of children she has had might be useful information only if it strongly influenced her self-esteem in the maternal role.

CLASSIFICATION

Competency Category:	Data Collection
Taxonomic Level:	Application
Client Age:	Adult
Nursing Practice:	Psychosocial Needs

REFERENCES
Olds et al. (1992), p. 185
Reeder et al. (1992), p. 1280

31 CORRECT ANSWER: 3

1. This entry does not mention the client's loss of pleasure with sexual relations.
2. The client has not stated that she is frigid.
3. **This entry into the nursing notes is appropriate; all information is charted correctly.**
4. This entry does not mention the client's loss of pleasure with sexual relations, and repeats information about fear of becoming pregnant.

CLASSIFICATION

Competency Category:	Data Collection
Taxonomic Level:	Application
Client Age:	Adult
Nursing Practice:	Professional Responsibilities

REFERENCES
Olds et al. (1992), pp. 186
Taber (1989), pp. 73-74, 545-546, 1106-1107

32 CORRECT ANSWER: 4

1. Maria has not mentioned anxiety or changes in body image.
2. Maria may be indirectly seeking knowledge about causes of pain, but there is no indication of changes in her sexual patterns. The change is in her sexual function.
3. Maria has not indicated that her self-esteem has been affected by her changing sexual patterns. She has identified pain as the problem.
4. Hormonal changes at menopause cause dryness and thinning of the vaginal mucous membrane, leading to pain during intercourse. This can be overcome with the use of water-soluble lubricants.

CLASSIFICATION

Competency Category:	Analysis & Interpretation of Data
Taxonomic Level:	Application
Client Age:	Adult
Nursing Practice:	Screening & Diagnosis

REFERENCES

Olds et al. (1992), p.186
Smeltzer & Bare (1992), p.1244

33 CORRECT ANSWER: 2

1. This is a closed-ended question, and will not determine if Maria has benefited from the medication. Also, Maria may not know what the side effects are.
2. This open-ended question allows Maria to tell the nurse about benefits and side effects of the medication.
3. This is a closed-ended question and will not determine the side effects Maria may be experiencing.
4. This is a closed-ended question, and will not determine if Maria is experiencing side effects.

CLASSIFICATION

Competency Category:	Implementation
Taxonomic Level:	Application
Client Age:	Adult
Nursing Practice:	Pharmacology

REFERENCES

Craven & Hirnle (1992), p. 284
Potter & Perry (1993), p. 153

34 CORRECT ANSWER: 3

1. The client's readiness to learn must be assessed prior to implementing the plan.
2. Evaluation should be done after implementation, and can be arranged once the client has thought about and reviewed the material.
3. Using materials the client understands is essential in ensuring comprehension and retention of information.
4. Asking the client about her current knowledge of the topic is part of the assessment of learning needs.

CLASSIFICATION

Competency Category:	Implementation
Taxonomic Level:	Application
Client Age:	Adult
Nursing Practice:	Communication

REFERENCES

Craven & Hirnle (1992), pp. 416-420
Potter & Perry (1993), pp. 366-377

35 CORRECT ANSWER: 2

1. Collecting pamphlets does not guarantee that the nurse will read the material.
2. Attending a workshop will enhance the nurse's knowledge of menopause and aging, and will provide suitable preparation for caring for Maria.
3. Talking to a co-worker is not the most appropriate action because each person's experience with menopause is different.
4. Asking Maria to share what she knows about menopause does nothing to expand the nurse's professional knowledge base.

CLASSIFICATION

Competency Category:	Professional Practice
Taxonomic Level:	Application
Client Age:	Adult
Nursing Practice:	Professional Responsibilities

REFERENCES

Craven & Hirnle (1992), p. 16
Taylor et al. (1993), p. 14

CASE 18

36 CORRECT ANSWER: 1

1. Tolerance for invasive procedures is increased by allowing time following the analgesic administration, prior to other procedures being performed.
2. A rest period should follow the analgesic injection to allow time for it to take effect before invasive procedures are initiated.
3. The most painful procedures should not be completed before the analgesic is given.
4. The analgesic should be given before any invasive procedures are initiated.

CLASSIFICATION

Competency Category:	Implementation
Taxonomic Level:	Application
Client Age:	Adult
Nursing Practice:	Clinical Techniques

REFERENCES

Potter & Perry (1993), p. 776
Smeltzer & Bare (1992), p. 60

37 CORRECT ANSWER: 3

1. An incorrect formula calculation was used or an error was made in the calculation.
2. An incorrect formula calculation was used or an error was made in the calculation.
3.
$$\frac{\text{Dose available}}{\text{Volume of solution available}} = \frac{\text{Dose desired}}{\text{Volume required}}$$

$$\frac{250 \text{ mg}}{5 \text{ mL}} = \frac{25 \text{ mg}}{\text{Volume required}}$$

$$\frac{250}{5} = \frac{25}{x}$$

Cross multiply: $250\,x = 125$

$$x = \frac{125}{250} = 0.50 \text{ mL}$$

4. An incorrect formula calculation was used or an error was made in the calculation.

CLASSIFICATION

Competency Category:	Implementation
Taxonomic Level:	Application
Client Age:	Adult
Nursing Practice:	Pharmacology

REFERENCES

Duff (1992), p. 66
Potter & Perry (1993), pp. 626-627

38 CORRECT ANSWER: 4

1. Removal and replacement of the catheter would be done only after other less invasive actions had failed.
2. Irrigating the catheter would not be done first. This procedure usually requires a physician's order.
3. The client has a closed drainage system which should not be opened.
4. The nurse should first check for an external obstruction affecting the drainage tube before taking other actions.

CLASSIFICATION

Competency Category:	Implementation
Taxonomic Level:	Application
Client Age:	Adult
Nursing Practice:	Clinical Techniques

REFERENCES

Phipps et al. (1991), p. 1445
Smeltzer & Bare (1991), p. 669

39 CORRECT ANSWER: 3

1. The rate should not be constant. For the first 15 minutes, the transfusion should be infused slowly, and then the rate increased.
2. A slow infusion will not avoid a transfusion reaction, and may interfere with completing the transfusion on time.
3. Most transfusion reactions occur within the first few minutes so transfusion rates are increased after 15 minutes.
4. The pressure appliance damages the red blood cells and is only used in emergencies.

CLASSIFICATION

Competency Category:	Implementation
Taxonomic Level:	Application
Client Age:	Adult
Nursing Practice:	Clinical Techniques

REFERENCES

Craven & Hirnle (1992), p. 884
Ignatavicius & Bayne (1991), p. 2258

40 CORRECT ANSWER: 2

1. It is unrealistic to ask a relative to remain with the client 24 hours a day.
2. The nurse should first make an assessment of the client's requirements for supervision and then provide them as necessary.
3. It would breach confidentiality to discuss the client's status with the other clients.
4. Labeling the client with a sign represents a breach of confidentiality and shows a lack of respect.

CLASSIFICATION

Competency Category:	Implementation
Taxonomic Level:	Application
Client Age:	Adult
Nursing Practice:	Physiological Needs

REFERENCES

Castiglia & Harben (1992), p. 452
Smeltzer & Bare (1991), pp. 1502, 1506

41 CORRECT ANSWER: 4

1. A saline enema would not likely facilitate evacuation of the large, hard mass.
2. The use of a laxative would cause bowel cramping without removing the fecal mass from the rectum.
3. The problem is fecal impaction, not constipation.
4. The appropriate method for fecal disimpaction is to remove the feces manually with a lubricated, gloved finger.

CLASSIFICATION

Competency Category:	Implementation
Taxonomic Level:	Knowledge/Comprehension
Client Age:	Adult
Nursing Practice:	Clinical Techniques

REFERENCES

Phipps et al. (1991), p. 1305
Smeltzer & Bare (1991), p. 59

CASE 19

42 CORRECT ANSWER: 1

1. Discussing the nursing diagnoses with the client and her family validates the nurse's findings and ensures that all the client's needs are addressed.
2. The nursing diagnoses themselves will not give Mrs. Smith's family skills for assisting her.
3. Discussing the nursing diagnoses with Mrs. Smith and her family may provide some emotional support but this is not the main reason for these discussions.
4. There are many other ways to interact with the client and her family. This is not an important reason to discuss the nursing diagnoses.

CLASSIFICATION

Competency Category:	Analysis & Interpretation of Data
Taxonomic Level:	Critical Thinking
Client Age:	Older Adult
Nursing Practice:	Communication

REFERENCES

Birchenall & Streight (1993), pp. 250, 252
Smeltzer & Bare (1992), p. 1713

43 CORRECT ANSWER: 4

1. Although ineffective coping is a problem for many Parkinsonian clients, there is no evidence to support this nursing diagnosis for Mrs. Smith.
2. Although activity intolerance related to motor dysfunction is an ongoing problem with Parkinsonian clients, impaired physical mobility must be addressed before activity intolerance can be decreased.
3. Although self-care deficit is a major problem for Mrs. Smith and her family, impaired physical mobility must be addressed before she is able to improve her ability to care for herself.
4. Interventions related to impaired physical mobility will assist Mrs. Smith to improve strength, stamina, and range of motion. It is necessary to improve her physical mobility as a first step toward improving her self-care deficit.

CLASSIFICATION

Competency Category:	Planning Care
Taxonomic Level:	Critical Thinking
Client Age:	Older Adult
Nursing Practice:	Screening & Diagnosis

REFERENCES

Birchenall & Streight (1993), pp. 248-249, 253
Smeltzer & Bare (1992), pp. 1712-1713

44 CORRECT ANSWER: 3

1. Mrs. Smith should be encouraged to ambulate to the bathroom with assistance. Assisting her onto the bedpan is not appropriate at this time.
2. Bedside rails are used to assist the client to turn when in bed, not as a safety precaution at this stage of Parkinson's disease.
3. Client's with Parkinson's disease experience swallowing difficulties and decreased cough reflex. Placing Mrs. Smith in an upright position decreases the danger of aspiration.
4. Exercise, with assistance, should be encouraged for clients with Parkinson's disease. Confining Mrs. Smith to her room hinders this goal.

CLASSIFICATION

Competency Category:	Implementation
Taxonomic Level:	Application
Client Age:	Older Adult
Nursing Practice:	Physiological Needs

REFERENCES
Birchenall & Streight (1993), p. 249
Smeltzer & Bare (1992), pp.1712-1713

45 CORRECT ANSWER: 3

1. Thin liquids should be avoided because of the danger of aspiration in clients with Parkinson's disease.
2. A diet based on her favorite foods will not necessarily provide Mrs. Smith with her nutritional requirements.
3. A semisolid diet lessens the chance of aspiration in clients with Parkinson's disease.
4. Parkinsonian clients have an increased need for carbohydrates as weight loss is a problem.

CLASSIFICATION

Competency Category:	Implementation
Taxonomic Level:	Application
Client Age:	Older Adult
Nursing Practice:	Physiological Needs

REFERENCES
Lewis & Collier (1992), p. 1604
Smeltzer & Bare (1992), p. 1713

46 CORRECT ANSWER: 3

1. Dyskinesias (abnormal involuntary movements) will not lessen as they are fairly common side effects of levodopa/carbidopa (Sinemet) therapy.
2. Depression will not decrease as it is a major side effect of levidopa/carbidopa (Sinemet).
3. Levodopa/carbidopa (Sinemet) improves the depleted dopamine levels in the CNS and decreases bradykinesia and rigidity.
4. Hallucinations and sleep disturbances will not decrease as they are side effects of levodopa/carbidopa (Sinemet).

CLASSIFICATION

Competency Category:	Analysis & Interpretation of Data
Taxonomic Level:	Knowledge/Comprehension
Client Age:	Older Adult
Nursing Practice:	Pharmacology

REFERENCES
Lewis & Collier (1992), p. 1602
Smeltzer & Bare (1992), p. 1711

47 CORRECT ANSWER: 3

1. Although the dietitian and pharmacist are involved in the plan of care, they are not the most appropriate sources of information regarding activities of daily living.
2. The nurses' notes are a valuable tool for data collection, but are not the best source of information for the ongoing assessment of activities of daily living.
3. Both the physical and the occupational therapist test the client's ability to perform self-care activities and intervene to maintain and/or restore maximal function.
4. While the social worker and the speech therapist are important sources of information in the overall assessment of Mrs. Smith, they are not appropriate sources of information for assessing the ability to carry out activities of daily living.

CLASSIFICATION

Competency Category:	Data Collection
Taxonomic Level:	Knowledge/Comprehension
Client Age:	Older Adult
Nursing Practice:	Professional Responsibilities

REFERENCES

Birchenall & Streight (1993), pp. 173-174
Smeltzer & Bare (1992), p. 218

CASE 20

48 CORRECT ANSWER: 4

1. Speaking in a quiet tone of voice does not ensure privacy.
2. Discussing Judy's care with her is not an invasion of Judy's privacy.
3. Asking the students how Judy's privacy can be maintained does not ensure that privacy will be maintained.
4. Pulling the curtain around Judy's bed when interviewing her ensures her privacy.

CLASSIFICATION

Competency Category:	Professional Practice
Taxonomic Level:	Application
Client Age:	Child & Adolescent
Nursing Practice:	Professional Responsibilities

REFERENCES

Kozier et al. (1991), p. 97
Potter & Perry (1993), pp. 295-296

49 CORRECT ANSWER: 2

1. While rest is important, pain control is a priority during transition and may promote rest.
2. Pain control is a priority need during transition.
3. While social support is important, pain control is a priority during transition.
4. While bowel elimination is important, pain control is a priority during transition.

CLASSIFICATION

Competency Category:	Planning Care
Taxonomic Level:	Application
Client Age:	Child & Adolescent
Nursing Practice:	Physiological Needs

REFERENCES

May & Mahlmeister (1990), p. 618
Olds et al. (1992), pp. 596-597

50 CORRECT ANSWER: 3

1. Offering Judy a bedpan may compromise the safety of the fetus at this time.
2. Providing sedation would not enhance labor at this time. Anxiety and restlessness are characteristic signs of this phase.
3. Meconium staining in a fetus in a vertex presentation may denote signs of fetal distress. Therefore, assessment of the fetal heart rate should be carried out immediately after the rupture of membranes.
4. Determining the position of the fetus does not provide immediate information about the condition of the fetus.

CLASSIFICATION

Competency Category:	Implementation
Taxonomic Level:	Application
Client Age:	Child & Adolescent
Nursing Practice:	Clinical Techniques

REFERENCES
May & Mahlmeister (1990), p. 580
Olds et al. (1992), p. 662

51 CORRECT ANSWER: 3

1. Perineal hygiene is best promoted by frequent cleansing of the perineal area. A daily shower would not be sufficient.
2. A tub bath may increase chances for infection.
3. Frequent sitz baths promote comfort, healing, and hygiene to the perineal area.
4. A bed bath is the least effective method of promoting perineal hygiene.

CLASSIFICATION

Competency Category:	Implementation
Taxonomic Level:	Knowledge/Comprehension
Client Age:	Child & Adolescent
Nursing Practice:	Physiological Needs

REFERENCES
May & Mahlmeister (1990), p. 888
Olds et al. (1992), p. 1101

52 CORRECT ANSWER: 2

1. Asking another staff nurse if the teaching was done is not likely to provide the desired information.
2. The nursing notes are considered to be a legal record. If the student has recorded the teaching, the nurse may conclude that it was done.
3. Asking the other client in the room if the teaching was done is not as reliable as the client chart, and may violate client confidentiality.
4. Asking the nurse coming on duty to ask Judy if she received the teaching would not be the nurse's first action; the client record should be consulted first.

CLASSIFICATION

Competency Category:	Evaluation
Taxonomic Level:	Critical Thinking
Client Age:	Child & Adolescent
Nursing Practice:	Professional Responsibilities

REFERENCES
Kozier et al. (1991), p. 298
Potter & Perry (1993), p. 696

INDEPENDENT ITEMS

53 CORRECT ANSWER: 1

1. Introducing self and explaining the nurse's role in client care helps the client know what to expect and may decrease anxiety, thus facilitating the nurse-client relationship.
2. To begin a health history interview, it would be more professional for the nurse to make a verbal introduction.
3. Adult clients may or may not prefer to have a relative present during the health interview and should be consulted as to their preference.
4. The client does not need to remove street clothes for the purposes of the health history, only for the physical exam which follows the interview and history-taking. Allowing the client to remain in his clothes during the initial interview facilitates the comfort level.

CLASSIFICATION

Competency Category:	Data Collection
Taxonomic Level:	Application
Client Age:	Adult
Nursing Practice:	Communication

REFERENCES

Kozier et al. (1991), pp. 177, 180
Potter & Perry (1993), p. 149

54 CORRECT ANSWER: 3

1. The effectiveness cannot be determined for approximately 20-45 minutes; therefore, documentation should be the nurse's next step.
2. Assessing should be completed prior to preparation and administration of the medication, not after.
3. As long as safety is not compromised, the next action should be documentation to ensure accuracy and completeness of the intervention.
4. Prior to verbally reporting administration, written documentation should be completed.

CLASSIFICATION

Competency Category:	Implementation
Taxonomic Level:	Knowledge/Comprehension
Client Age:	Adult
Nursing Practice:	Pharmacology

REFERENCES

Kozier et al. (1991), pp. 312-313, 976
Potter & Perry (1993), p. 697

55 CORRECT ANSWER: 1

1. A child of 10 is capable of offering an explanation and further information. This should be the nurse's first source for additional information.
2. The client should be the first source of information.
3. There is no evidence that the mother is present to provide immediate information. Also, the mother may not know the details as well as the child.
4. There is not enough information at this time to warrant a call to the physician.

CLASSIFICATION

Competency Category:	Data Collection
Taxonomic Level:	Application
Client Age:	Child & Adolescent
Nursing Practice:	Screening & Diagnosis

REFERENCES

Castiglia & Harben (1992), pp. 82-83
Whaley & Wong (1993), pp. 109-111

56 CORRECT ANSWER: 4

1.   Although the nurse is not ethically responsible
     for complying with the request, the nurse
     should communicate these feelings in a more
     respectful manner to the nursing supervisor.
2.   Offering someone else's services to provide
     care is inappropriate.
3.   Caring for a client who undergoes a therapeutic
     abortion is not outside the nurse's area of
     expertise.
4.   The nurse is expressing feelings precisely, and
     is indicating a willingness to accept another
     assignment.

CLASSIFICATION

Competency Category:	Professional Practice
Taxonomic Level:	Affective
Client Age:	General
Nursing Practice:	Professional Responsibilities

REFERENCES
Canadian Nurses Association (1991), p. 10
Craven & Hirnle (1992), pp. 46-47

57 CORRECT ANSWER: 2

1.   Although administering an antiemetic is an
     appropriate action, the I.V. should not be
     discontinued until its effectiveness can be
     evaluated.
2.   The nurse should maintain the I.V. and contact
     the physician about Mrs. Carson's need for
     ongoing monitoring which should occur in
     hospital.
3.   The home care program is not designed to
     provide the frequent monitoring required by
     Mrs. Carson at this time.
4.   This action is premature; Mrs. Carson's plan
     of care should first be modified.

CLASSIFICATION

Competency Category:	Professional Practice
Taxonomic Level:	Critical Thinking
Client Age:	Older Adult
Nursing Practice:	Clinical Techniques

REFERENCES
Black & Matassarin-Jabocs (1993), pp. 399-400
Potter & Perry (1993), pp. 1602-1603, 1639

58 CORRECT ANSWER: 2

1.   There is less accuracy using a spoon to
     measure the medication. As well, there is
     a possibility of breakage of the spoon if the
     child clamps down in a bite.
2.   The syringe provides a reliable measure
     and a convenient means of transport.
3.   The dropper is an unreliable device for
     measuring liquids. The volume of the drop
     varies according to the viscosity of the liquid.
4.   A child of 6 months is likely not used to
     drinking from a cup. As well, it is hard to
     determine accuracy with small doses since
     some of the liquid clings to the side of the cup.

CLASSIFICATION

Competency Category:	Implementation
Taxonomic Level:	Knowledge/Comprehension
Client Age:	Child & Adolescent
Nursing Practice:	Pharmacology

REFERENCES
Mott et al. (1990), p. 892
Whaley & Wong (1993), pp. 671-674

59 CORRECT ANSWER: 4

1. Eating all the food on the tray indicates that the client has a good appetite and does not indicate readiness to learn.
2. This statement reflects a lack of knowledge and not readiness to learn.
3. Discussing a friend with diabetes indicates that the client may have some knowledge of diabetes based on previous experience, but does not indicate readiness to learn.
4. One indication of the readiness to learn is when the client seeks out information by asking related questions.

CLASSIFICATION

Competency Category:	Analysis & Interpretation of Data
Taxonomic Level:	Application
Client Age:	Adult
Nursing Practice:	Communication

REFERENCES

Kozier et al. (1991), p. 284
Potter & Perry (1993), p. 361

60 CORRECT ANSWER: 4

1. Calling Jay's family could compromise client confidentiality.
2. Filing a report with the security department does not share the information with the health team.
3. The nurse could report the incident to the physician at a later time, not immediately.
4. Written documentation is the best way to monitor Jay consistently for further behaviors and to communicate with the rest of the team.

CLASSIFICATION

Competency Category:	Planning Care
Taxonomic Level:	Application
Client Age:	Adult
Nursing Practice:	Professional Responsibilities

REFERENCES

Craven & Hirnle (1992), pp. 155-156
Potter & Perry (1993), p. 719

61 CORRECT ANSWER: 4

1. The side effect of furosemide which should be monitored is hypokalemia.
2. Urine specific gravity is not routinely indicated in diuretic therapy.
3. Excessive weight loss is the more likely effect.
4. Clients receiving furosemide, particularly when administered per I.V., should be observed for postural hypotension.

CLASSIFICATION

Competency Category:	Implementation
Taxonomic Level:	Application
Client Age:	Older Adult
Nursing Practice:	Pharmacology

REFERENCES

Shannon & Wislon (1992), pp. 199-200
Skidmore-Roth (1993), pp. 446-447

62 CORRECT ANSWER: 3

1. Data collection, identifying problems, and evaluation are not steps in planning care. Goals should be set in collaboration with the client.
2. Assessment, problem identification and formulating diagnosis are not steps in planning care. Goal setting should be done in collaboration with the client.
3. All steps of planning care are clearly identified in this sequence of activities.
4. These are other steps of the nursing process, not the steps of planning care.

CLASSIFICATION

Competency Category:	Planning Care
Taxonomic Level:	Knowledge/Comprehension
Client Age:	General
Nursing Practice:	Professional Responsibilities

REFERENCES

Olds et al. (1992), p. 12
Potter & Perry (1993), p. 188

63 CORRECT ANSWER: 3

1. The community health nurse may not know Mrs. Holmes' situation and would not be able to respond to her questions without speaking to her physician or the hospital nurse. Even though the community health nurse has Mrs. Holmes' phone number, the client and her family have not been adequately prepared for discharge.
2. It is unfair and unreasonable to expect the client and her family to be prepared for discharge when teaching is done on the same day.
3. The nurse acts as a client advocate by requesting a delay in discharge until satisfactory arrangements can be made for client follow-up care.
4. The family should be prepared and have a chance to ask questions prior to taking Mrs. Holmes home.

CLASSIFICATION

Competency Category:	Professional Practice
Taxonomic Level:	Critical Thinking
Client Age:	Older Adult
Nursing Practice:	Professional Responsibilities

REFERENCES

Potter & Perry (1993), p. 23
Smeltzer & Bare (1992), p. 13

64 CORRECT ANSWER: 3

1. This is true, but it also presents a condescending attitude to Kim. It does not answer her question.
2. It may be true that it is a hospital policy; however, this answer may not satisfy Kim.
3. This is one of the major reasons for electronic fetal monitoring during induction.
4. This response may give Kim undue cause for alarm. Despite all its capabilities, the electronic fetal monitor does not give the staff plenty of time to deliver the baby.

CLASSIFICATION

Competency Category:	Implementation
Taxonomic Level:	Application
Client Age:	Adult
Nursing Practice:	Screening & Diagnosis

REFERENCES

Olds et al. (1992), pp. 625-627
Reeder et al. (1992), pp. 925, 1105

65 CORRECT ANSWER: 2

1. Objective data can only be collected by directly observing the client's behavior. Subjective data are obtained by speaking with family members.
2. Clients with mild cognitive dysfunction can better understand direct questions with limited choices. The assessment phase should be modified in this manner.
3. Generalizing uncooperativeness from the initial contact would be premature. Uncooperativeness may not be the reason for the client's behavior.
4. Although additional information from the health care team would be helpful, the nurse must first collect data from the client to determine her current status.

CLASSIFICATION

Competency Category:	Data Collection
Taxonomic Level:	Application
Client Age:	Older Adult
Nursing Practice:	Communication

REFERENCES

Birchenall & Streight (1993), p. 266
Kozier et al. (1991), p. 175

66 CORRECT ANSWER: 2

1. This is incorrect because it does not follow the proper line of authority. The nurse's immediate supervisor should be informed first.
2. Since the nurse has already been reprimanded by the head nurse, it is important that this authority be made aware of the continuing problems.
3. The nurse has already been reprimanded. Therefore, the next level of authority has to be involved.
4. This action is appropriate for short-term client safety; to ensure long-term client safety, the incident must be reported.

CLASSIFICATION

Competency Category:	Professional Practice
Taxonomic Level:	Knowledge/Comprehension
Client Age:	Child & Adolescent
Nursing Practice:	Professional Responsibilities

REFERENCES

Potter & Perry (1993), p. 23
Smeltzer & Bare (1992), p. 10

67 CORRECT ANSWER: 3

1. Referring the client to the hospital's bereavement counselor does not respond to the immediate concern of the client. Mrs. Evans needs to talk further about her loss.
2. Informing Mrs. Evans' daughter that her mother is still grieving is inappropriate because it is not helpful for Mrs. Evans now, and her daughter is probably already aware that her mother is resolving grief.
3. In first-level empathy, nurses should communicate that they have listened to what was said. Also, by encouraging the client to express her feelings, the nurse deomonstrates a helping attitude.
4. While sharing of similar circumstances can be helpful, this response assumes that Mrs. Evans wants to meet another client in a similar situation.

CLASSIFICATION

Competency Category:	Implementation
Taxonomic Level:	Affective
Client Age:	Adult
Nursing Practice:	Psychosocial Needs

REFERENCES

Kozier et al. (1991), pp. 245-246
Taylor et al. (1993), p. 329

68 CORRECT ANSWER: 2

1. Monitoring intake and output is an important nursing responsibility but does nothing to maintain the I.V. therapy.
2. Assessing the insertion site is necessary to ensure that the fluid is running into the vein and not into the surrounding tissues.
3. Labeling the I.V. bag when medications are added is also an important nursing responsibility but does nothing to maintain the I.V. therapy.
4. The I.V. rate should be administered as ordered. Although the client is elderly, the nurse should not assume that she cannot tolerate or does not need a more rapid intake of fluid.

CLASSIFICATION

Competency Category:	Implementation
Taxonomic Level:	Application
Client Age:	Older Adult
Nursing Practice:	Clinical Techniques

REFERENCES

Kozier et al. (1991), p. 1078
Taylor et al. (1993), pp. 1045, 1049

69 CORRECT ANSWER: 3

1. It is not necessary to wear a gown and gloves when providing care to Jenny because handwashing is sufficient to prevent cross-contamination in an immunocompromised client.
2. Neutropenia does not predispose a client to bleeding. Soft-sponged toothbrushes are more appropriate for clients with thrombocytopenia.
3. Because the mouth is a prime source for infection in the immunocompromised client, antiseptic mouthwashes are ordered to prevent this problem.
4. There is no indication that a venipuncture would be detrimental for Jenny. This would be an appropriate action for clients with thrombocytopenia.

CLASSIFICATION

Competency Category:	Analysis & Interpretation of Data
Taxonomic Level:	Application
Client Age:	General
Nursing Practice:	Physiological Needs

REFERENCES

Baird (1991), pp. 744, 751-752
Whaley & Wong (1993), p. 1675

70 CORRECT ANSWER: 1

1. Standards of practice are established by the professional associations to guide nurses in their practice of nursing.
2. Practice is measured against standards set by professional associations; practice should not be measured in comparison to an expert.
3. Although a letter of commendation is personally rewarding for the nurse, the public does not set the standards of practice for a profession.
4. Delegation of nursing functions to non-nursing personnel contravenes nursing standards.

CLASSIFICATION

Competency Category:	Professional Practice
Taxonomic Level:	Knowledge/Comprehension
Client Age:	General
Nursing Practice:	Professional Responsibilities

REFERENCES

Potter & Perry (1993), p. 868
Taylor et al. (1993), p. 84

71 CORRECT ANSWER: 1

1. For the hypertensive client, a drop of 30 mmHg below baseline systolic pressure may be a sign of shock. Because of her age and the fact that she is receiving a beta blocker, Mrs. Cross may not have an increased pulse rate. Further assessment is needed to confirm the nurse's suspicions.
2. Asking Mrs. Cross to stand is inappropriate. Normal changes in postural hypotension combined with the existing drop in baseline would make this option unsafe for the client.
3. Because the client has been on metoprolol (Lopressor) for 10 months, it is unlikely that the medication is the reason for the excessive drop in blood pressure. Further assessment is required immediately.
4. Reporting to the physician without further assessment data would be premature.

CLASSIFICATION

Competency Category:	Evaluation
Taxonomic Level:	Critical Thinking
Client Age:	Adult
Nursing Practice:	Pharmacology

REFERENCES
Shannon & Wislon (1992), p. 773
Lewis & Collier (1992), pp. 745-746

72 CORRECT ANSWER: 4

1. The nurse has to assess the appropriateness of touch (e.g., Rita may be frightened by premature touching or may perceive touching as aggressive) before using it to facilitate participation.
2. The formality of a conference room is not conducive to fostering a sharing or participative environment.
3. Rita needs ownership of the teaching plan to enhance the implementation. Frequently, adolescents are more willing to discuss their concerns outside the family rather than with a parent present.
4. Giving Rita the choice recognizes the independence of adolescents.

CLASSIFICATION

Competency Category:	Planning Care
Taxonomic Level:	Application
Client Age:	Child & Adolescent
Nursing Practice:	Psychosocial Needs

REFERENCES
Castiglia & Harben (1992), p. 343
Whaley & Wong (1993), pp. 109-113

73 CORRECT ANSWER: 2

1. Anxiety lowers the pain threshold.
2. As a client with cancer may experience breakthrough pain, p.r.n. medication may be required over and above around-the-clock administrations.
3. Addiction is not a relevant issue in clients with terminal cancer.
4. Pain control for the client with terminal cancer should be justified by the client's level of pain, not by the frequency of the dose.

CLASSIFICATION

Competency Category:	Implementation
Taxonomic Level:	Critical Thinking
Client Age:	General
Nursing Practice:	Pharmacology

REFERENCES
Baird et al. (1991), p. 795
Otto (1991), p. 398

74 CORRECT ANSWER: 4

1. Incorporation of knowledge into the care plan is not the first step in using new nursing knowledge. This new knowledge should be shared with other members of the health care team.
2. The physician is an important member of the health care team, but all decisions regarding client care do not lie with the physician.
3. Accepting professional responsibility is important, but incorporating this new knowledge into the client's plan of care is not the first step.
4. Offering to do an education session followed by discussion complies with the professional guideline of incorporating new knowledge into agency policy and procedures before implementation.

CLASSIFICATION

Competency Category:	Professional Practice
Taxonomic Level:	Application
Client Age:	Child & Adolescent
Nursing Practice:	Professional Responsibilities

REFERENCES
Kozier et al. (1991), p. 33
Potter & Perry (1993), pp. 250-251

75 CORRECT ANSWER: 2

1. Renting a hospital bed is unnecessary because he can use his own bed.
2. Buying loose fitting clothes will accommodate the cast around the waist and leg.
3. Because he has a hip spica with an extension to one leg, he is unable to bend at the waist and cannot use a wheelchair.
4. A home care worker is not necessary as his parents will be taught how to safely turn him.

CLASSIFICATION

Competency Category:	Implementation
Taxonomic Level:	Application
Client Age:	Child & Adolescent
Nursing Practice:	Physiological Needs

REFERENCES
Marlow & Redding (1988), pp. 534, 822
Mott et al. (1990), pp. 1573-1574

76 CORRECT ANSWER: 1

1. This introduction respects the right of the client to be addressed properly and indicates the nurse's professional capacity.
2. This may be a true statement, but it does not focus on the nurse-client relationship.
3. Calling the client by his first name does not show respect for an elderly person.
4. This statement does not show respect for an elderly client. The nurse does not identify professional status.

CLASSIFICATION

Competency Category:	Data Collection
Taxonomic Level:	Application
Client Age:	Older Adult
Nursing Practice:	Communication

REFERENCES
Kozier et al. (1991), pp. 180, 244
Smith (1992), pp. 103-104

77 CORRECT ANSWER: 2

1. Asking the client what she thinks she may be doing incorrectly implies that her skin problem is her fault and may undermine her confidence in her ability to provide her own care.
2. Having the client change her colostomy pouch will enable the nurse to evaluate the client's technique; if changes are advisable, the nurse can coach the client as she proceeds.
3. While use of a skin barrier/paste around the stoma is an appropriate action to protect red tender skin, the nurse should avoid performing the care for the client as this will discourage the client's self-care.
4. While gentle cleansing and drying of the skin around the stoma are correct actions, the nurse should avoid performing the care for the client as this will discourage the client's self-care.

CLASSIFICATION

Competency Category:	Implementation
Taxonomic Level:	Application
Client Age:	Adult
Nursing Practice:	Clinical Techniques

REFERENCES
Kozier et al. (1991), p. 293
Phipps et al. (1991), pp. 1340-1345

78 CORRECT ANSWER: 2

1. When the client is in early shock, immediate intervention is required; therefore, documentation is not the appropriate response.
2. Consulting the physician in the early stage of shock will facilitate timely intervention before shock progresses.
3. Sims' position is inappropriate for early shock.
4. Reassessing implies that the nurse intends to leave the client in this condition for another 30 minutes; this action could be life-threatening as he needs constant supervision as well as reassessment.

CLASSIFICATION

Competency Category:	Implementation
Taxonomic Level:	Application
Client Age:	Adult
Nursing Practice:	Screening & Diagnosis

REFERENCES
Ignatavicius & Bayne (1991), p. 405
Phipps et al. (1991), pp. 578-579

79 CORRECT ANSWER: 4

1. The nurse needs to look at other options to solve this problem instead of relying on staff on the next shift, who may also be very busy.
2. Informing the nursing supervisor that the usual workload in the ICU consists of 2 clients per shift implies that the nurse is not willing to care for more than 2 clients, and is unwilling to work as a member of the health care team.
3. Prioritizing care is appropriate; however, the families should not be relied upon to lighten the nurse's workload.
4. By consulting the nursing supervisor, the nurse recognizes a problem and goes through the proper channels to get help. As well, the nurse delegates responsibility, taking into consideration the expertise of the health care aide.

CLASSIFICATION

Competency Category:	Professional Practice
Taxonomic Level:	Critical Thinking
Client Age:	General
Nursing Practice:	Professional Responsibilities

REFERENCES

Potter & Perry (1993), p. 200
Smith (1992), pp. 177-178

80 CORRECT ANSWER: 4

1. The nurse should address the client's concern for further elaboration before approaching the team for assistance.
2. Cancelling the order for the medication is inappropriate until the nursing and medical staff ascertain that the client has the appropriate information on which to base her refusal.
3. Agreeing to take the medication does not address the client's identified concern about the medication. This meets the nurse's goal rather than the client's.
4. If the nurse is modifying the plan of care for further knowledge assessment, the expected outcome must relate to the client's knowledge level as this statement does.

CLASSIFICATION

Competency Category:	Implementation
Taxonomic Level:	Application
Client Age:	Adult
Nursing Practice:	Pharmacology

REFERENCES

Kozier et al. (1991), p. 211
Potter & Perry (1993), pp. 190-191

81 CORRECT ANSWER: 3

1. Diuretics should be taken early in the day so that sleep will be promoted at night.
2. While getting up slowly may be an appropriate nursing intervention for someone taking a diuretic, it does not address the client's concern.
3. Taking a diuretic early in the day will increase the probability that peak action will occur before nighttime.
4. Advising the client to change the dosage of medication is beyond the scope of nursing practice.

CLASSIFICATION

Competency Category:	Planning Care
Taxonomic Level:	Application
Client Age:	Adult
Nursing Practice:	Pharmacology

REFERENCES

Baer & Williams (1992), p. 573
Canadian Pharmaceutical Association (1994), p. 676

82 CORRECT ANSWER: 3

1. Malignant hypertension accompanied by a headache and blurred vision may lead to stroke or heart failure. This client's symptoms constitute a medical emergency. It is unsafe to allow this client to wait 4 hours to be seen by a physician.
2. This question may produce the desired effect (i.e., having the physician see the client), but it is aggressive rather than assertive.
3. To maintain client safety and fulfil one's role as a client advocate, the nurse's best response is to state to the physician that the client must be seen now. Asking "Who should I call?" informs the physician in a non-confrontational way that the nurse will ensure that this client is seen as soon as possible.
4. Requesting an order for additional medication is an inappropriate response. The client may require treatment beyond that which can be rendered on a general nursing unit.

CLASSIFICATION

Competency Category:	Professional Practice
Taxonomic Level:	Critical Thinking
Client Age:	General
Nursing Practice:	Professional Responsibilities

REFERENCES

Ignatavicius & Bayne (1991), p. 2196
Phipps et al. (1991), p. 765

83 CORRECT ANSWER: 2

1. Isolating a client in a private room does not in itself prevent infection.
2. Practicing wound and skin precautions is the most effective intervention in preventing infections.
3. A culture and sensitivity report of a swab of a burn wound will reveal the presence of infection, but will not prevent infection.
4. Having client families provide play materials would not prevent infection as effectively as practicing wound and skin precautions.

CLASSIFICATION

Competency Category:	Implementation
Taxonomic Level:	Application
Client Age:	Child & Adolescent
Nursing Practice:	Clinical Techniques

REFERENCES

Ignatavicius & Bayne (1991), p. 614

Smeltzer & Bare (1992), p. 1901

84 CORRECT ANSWER: 3

1. Palpation of the abdomen should be deferred due to pain and tenderness associated with peritonitis.
2. Palpation and percussion of the abdomen should be deferred due to pain and tenderness associated with peritonitis.
3. Inspection and gentle auscultation would constitute a thorough abdominal assessment of the client with peritonitis. Both techniques will generate pertinent assessment data without causing client discomfort.
4. Percussion of the abdomen should be deferred due to pain and tenderness associated with peritonitis.

CLASSIFICATION

Competency Category:	Data Collection
Taxonomic Level:	Application
Client Age:	General
Nursing Practice:	Screening & Diagnosis

REFERENCES

Kozier et al. (1991), pp. 416-418.

Potter & Perry (1993), pp. 579-581

85 CORRECT ANSWER: 1

1. Walking freely in his room represents an appropriate activity level for a client 4 days post-MI.
2. Performing isometric exercises q.i.d does not provide an appropriate level of activity for Mr. Grey.
3. Walking up one flight of stairs is too demanding for Mr. Grey's heart.
4. Ambulating the full length of the corridor at this time would be too demanding for Mr. Grey's heart.

CLASSIFICATION

Competency Category:	Planning Care
Taxonomic Level:	Application
Client Age:	Older Adult
Nursing Practice:	Physiological Needs

REFERENCES

Black & Matassarin-Jabocs (1993), p. 1158

Phipps et al. (1991), p. 717

86 CORRECT ANSWER: 3

1. When information is communicated from one person to another, the original information may become distorted.
2. Communicating information through a one-to-one method is too time consuming for the nurse.
3. A meeting of the health care workers involved in the client's care will ensure that information is shared with the appropriate people. The meeting also encourages discussion, introduction of new information, and possible revision of the teaching plan.
4. A note on the front of the client's chart does not ensure that everyone involved with the client will get the information.

CLASSIFICATION

Competency Category:	Collaboration & Coordination
Taxonomic Level:	Application
Client Age:	General
Nursing Practice:	Professional Responsibilities

REFERENCES

Kozier et al. (1991), p. 28
Potter & Perry (1993), pp. 24-25

87 CORRECT ANSWER: 4

1. Referring Jane to her physician avoids responsibility for providing the requested information.
2. Telling the client it is too early for her to have sexual relations is judgmental and not helpful.
3. Asking the client if her parents are aware of her sexual relations does not address her need for information.
4. Offering to sit and discuss birth control indicates that the nurse is receiving the client's message, and is prepared to discuss the whole issue nonjudgmentally.

CLASSIFICATION

Competency Category:	Implementation
Taxonomic Level:	Affective
Client Age:	Child & Adolescent
Nursing Practice:	Psychosocial Needs

REFERENCES

Arnold & Boggs (1989), pp. 216-225
Smith (1992), p. 93

88 CORRECT ANSWER: 4

1. Reporting to the physician does not address Pat's concern.
2. Suggesting a way around the policy does not take into consideration why the policy is in place. Also, if the nurse is not there in the evening, it could cause problems.
3. Referral to the social worker does not address Pat's concern.
4. Discussing the issue with the nursing supervisor identifies the nurse's ability to question policy through the proper channels of communication.

CLASSIFICATION

Competency Category:	Professional Practice
Taxonomic Level:	Critical Thinking
Client Age:	Child & Adolescent
Nursing Practice:	Professional Responsibilities

REFERENCES

Canadian Nurses Association (1991), p. 1
Kozier et al. (1991), pp. 8-9

89 CORRECT ANSWER: 4

1. Taking his vital signs will not relieve his dyspnea.
2. Ambulation will increase the body's demand for oxygen.
3. Assisting him to a supine position will increase his dyspnea.
4. Administering oxygen will ease his breathing.

CLASSIFICATION

Competency Category:	Implementation
Taxonomic Level:	Knowledge/Comprehension
Client Age:	Older Adult
Nursing Practice:	Physiological Needs

REFERENCES

Black & Matassarin-Jabocs (1993), p. 949

Potter & Perry (1993), pp. 1244-1245

90 CORRECT ANSWER: 1

1. The client is exhibiting symptoms of air embolism. Positioning the client on his left side is the priority to prevent air from entering the pulmonary circulation.
2. Deep breathing may help reduce the client's anxiety, but will not resolve the air embolism.
3. The total parenteral nutrition infusion rate should not be slowed down without a physician's order.
4. A Trendelenburg is favored over a high-Fowler's position to increase intrathoracic pressure, thereby reducing the amount of blood pulled into the vena cava during inhalation.

CLASSIFICATION

Competency Category:	Implementation
Taxonomic Level:	Application
Client Age:	Older Adult
Nursing Practice:	Physiological Needs

REFERENCES

Craven & Hirnle (1992), p. 926

Smeltzer & Bare (1992), p. 890

91 CORRECT ANSWER: 4

1. Instructing him on how to put on his clothes reduces his sense of control.
2. Helping him to dress reduces his potential for independence.
3. Selecting his clothes for him reduces his potential for independence.
4. His independence, control, and self-esteem are enhanced by offering him a choice of clothing.

CLASSIFICATION

Competency Category:	Implementation
Taxonomic Level:	Application
Client Age:	Older Adult
Nursing Practice:	Psychosocial Needs

REFERENCES

Birchenall & Streight (1993), p. 268

Carnevali & Patrick (1993), p. 301

92 CORRECT ANSWER: 3

1. Assessing clients' progress does not indicate self-assessment.
2. Requesting a peer review is secondary to identifying one's own limitations. It means the nurse is relying on data from others instead of self.
3. Recognizing limitations and seeking help is the basis of self-assessment.
4. Asking clients for their perceptions of care is not an example of self-assessment.

CLASSIFICATION

Competency Category:	Professional Practice
Taxonomic Level:	Critical Thinking
Client Age:	General
Nursing Practice:	Professional Responsibilities

REFERENCES
Ellis & Hartley (1992), pp. 398-399
Kozier et al. (1991), p. 11-12, 143

93 CORRECT ANSWER: 1

1. By awakening the child to administer the prescribed mask, the nurse is following the proper procedure as well as the principle of safe timing for the medication. The child's status indicates that the treatment is being effective and is not necessarily a sign that medication should be discontinued.
2. Monitoring the child's respiratory status would be an important intervention; however, withholding prescribed medication and permitting the child to sleep is inconsistent with the principle of administering the medication on time. Symptoms may worsen.
3. Allowing the child to sleep an additional hour does not follow the principle of administering the medication on time.
4. Skipping the medication dose and time is not a safe nursing action. The physician would need to be consulted for this to be acceptable.

CLASSIFICATION

Competency Category:	Implementation
Taxonomic Level:	Application
Client Age:	Child & Adolescent
Nursing Practice:	Pharmacology

REFERENCES
Kozier et al. (1991), pp. 1265-1266
Spencer et al. (1993), pp. 165-166

94 CORRECT ANSWER: 3

1. The nurse should not assume that the family wishes to be left alone with the deceased.
2. The family's assistance would be obtained only if they asked to help bathe the body; many families would not feel comfortable bathing the body of a deceased relative.
3. By remaining with the family while they view the body, the nurse is available to provide the family with emotional support, if they so desire.
4. Briefly viewing the body may not provide the family with adequate time to say goodbye.

CLASSIFICATION

Competency Category:	Implementation
Taxonomic Level:	Application
Client Age:	Older Adult
Nursing Practice:	Psychosocial Needs

REFERENCES

Phipps et al. (1991), p. 309
Potter & Perry (1993), p. 880

95 CORRECT ANSWER: 3

1. In metabolic acidosis, the pH would be below 7.35, the $PaCO_2$ would be within normal range and the HCO_3 would be less than 22 mEq/L.
2. In metabolic alkalosis, the pH would be above 7.45, the $PaCO_2$ would be within normal range or slightly elevated, and the HCO_3 would be above 26 mEq/L
3. In respiratory acidosis, the pH would be below 7.35, the $PaCO_2$ would be above 45 mmHg, and the HCO_3 would remain within normal range.
4. In respiratory alkalosis, the pH would be above 7.45, the $PaCO_2$ would be below 35 mmHg, and the HCO_3 would be within normal range or slightly decreased.

CLASSIFICATION

Competency Category:	Analysis & Interpretation of Data
Taxonomic Level:	Critical Thinking
Client Age:	Adult
Nursing Practice:	Screening & Diagnosis

REFERENCES

Black & Matassarin-Jabocs (1993), p. 880
Phipps et al. (1991), pp. 572-576

96 CORRECT ANSWER: 3

1. Cheese is high in cholesterol and may contribute to a blockage.
2. An increase in calcium will not make the heart stronger.
3. Red meat is high in cholesterol and saturated fats. Decreasing red meat would lower his chances of developing coronary artery disease.
4. Eating peanut butter would not lower cholesterol.

CLASSIFICATION

Competency Category:	Evaluation
Taxonomic Level:	Application
Client Age:	Older Adult
Nursing Practice:	Communication

REFERENCES

Black & Matassarin-Jabocs (1993), pp. 1149, 1285
Phipps et al. (1991), pp. 771, 1202

97 CORRECT ANSWER: 1

1. As a client advocate, the nurse should attempt to understand the client's behaviors. To do this, the nurse should explore with Mrs. Jessome why she is pulling out the tube.
2. Giving a sedative prior to the feeding will not determine why Mrs. Jessome is pulling out the tube.
3. By automatically following the physician's order, the nurse is not acting as an advocate for Mrs. Jessome.
4. This action does not determine why the client is trying to pull out the tube.

CLASSIFICATION

Competency Category:	Professional Practice
Taxonomic Level:	Critical Thinking
Client Age:	Adult
Nursing Practice:	Professional Responsibilities

REFERENCES
Carnevali & Patrick (1993), pp. 771, 1202
Kozier et al. (1991), p. 29

98 CORRECT ANSWER: 1

1. Pacing routines and activities promotes a better balance between sleep/rest and activity.
2. Having the client determine the care is inappropriate since important aspects of care may be omitted and omission of these aspects of care may hinder recovery.
3. Permitting the client to sleep, and delaying some nursing activities, may prevent the completion of some critical nursing activities.
4. Completing all pertinent care at once may tire the client unnecessarily.

CLASSIFICATION

Competency Category:	Implementation
Taxonomic Level:	Knowledge/Comprehension
Client Age:	Older Adult
Nursing Practice:	Physiological Needs

REFERENCES
Potter & Perry (1993), pp. 1166-1167
Taylor et al. (1993), p. 735

99 CORRECT ANSWER: 4

1. Suggesting that she visit the city's food bank is inappropriate because she has no way to transport food other than carrying it, she would not know what types of food are available, and she may still have to cook the food.
2. Even though she is going to the store, this does not address her difficulty with cooking.
3. Mrs. Ostrowski would not be able to transport or use large amounts of food and the food would still require preparation.
4. The charge for the meals is geared to the person's ability to pay and would provide her with nutritious food that is already cooked.

CLASSIFICATION

Competency Category:	Planning Care
Taxonomic Level:	Application
Client Age:	Older Adult
Nursing Practice:	Physiological Needs

REFERENCES
Carnevali & Patrick (1993), pp. 230-232
Ebersole & Hess (1990), pp. 167-169

100 CORRECT ANSWER: 3

1. This entry is incorrect as it does not include the client's response to the nursing interventions.
2. This entry is incorrect. Although it includes the client's responses, they are not specific and measurable.
3. This is the correct entry. A narrative note should include pertinent client behaviors and nursing activities throughout the shift. Each nursing action is followed by the client's response.
4. This entry is incorrect as it is not concise and includes irrelevant information.

CLASSIFICATION

Competency Category:	Implementation
Taxonomic Level:	Application
Client Age:	General
Nursing Practice:	Professional Responsibilities

REFERENCES
Craven & Hirnle (1992), p. 158
Kozier et al. (1991), p. 313

CASE 21

101 CORRECT ANSWER: 2

1. Knowledge of the basic food groups is too advanced an expectation for the beginning phase of dietary teaching.
2. Dietary planning should include information about food intake and physical activity so that appropriate changes can be made where indicated.
3. By providing the client with a meal plan, the nurse is unable to determine what adjustments need to be made in his usual eating patterns.
4. Recording only mealtime foods will exclude important information about food consumed between meals.

CLASSIFICATION

Competency Category:	Implementation
Taxonomic Level:	Application
Client Age:	Adult
Nursing Practice:	Communication

REFERENCES
Ignatavicius & Bayne (1991), pp. 1602-1606
Smeltzer & Bare (1992), pp. 1028-1029

102 CORRECT ANSWER: 4

1. Since the drug is given only once a day, an hour's delay in adminstration is acceptable.
2. The client's chart should indicate the exact time of administration.
3. The nurse should be with the client to confirm that the medication is taken.
4. An hour's delay in administration is acceptable. However, the fact that the administration was late and why it was late should be recorded.

CLASSIFICATION

Competency Category:	Implementation
Taxonomic Level:	Application
Client Age:	Adult
Nursing Practice:	Pharmacology

REFERENCES
Kozier et al. (1991), pp. 1268-1269
Taylor et al. (1993), p. 1203

103   CORRECT ANSWER: 1

1. Poor circulation to the feet in persons with diabetes leads to poor wound healing and gangrene. The toenails and calluses must be skilfully trimmed.
2. Exposing his feet could predispose the client to injury.
3. Daily, not weekly, inspection of the feet is necessary to initiate early treatment of injury.
4. The use of a heating pad is contraindicated due to the potential for thermal injury to the foot.

CLASSIFICATION

Competency Category:	Implementation
Taxonomic Level:	Application
Client Age:	Adult
Nursing Practice:	Physiological Needs

REFERENCES
Ignatavicius & Bayne (1991), p. 1616
Smeltzer & Bare (1992), p. 1063

104   CORRECT ANSWER: 2

1. Evaluation identifies both met and unmet goals.
2. Identifying factors that interfered with the achievement of nursing goals allows the nurse to decide if goals or interventions need to be changed.
3. Response to treatment is not necessarily a reflection of the achievement of nursing goals.
4. Unresolved nursing diagnoses should be referred to the nurse in the community, not to the family.

CLASSIFICATION

Competency Category:	Implementation
Taxonomic Level:	Application
Client Age:	Adult
Nursing Practice:	Professional Responsibilities

REFERENCES
Kozier et al. (1991), pp. 231-235
Potter & Perry (1993), p. 223

105   CORRECT ANSWER: 4

1. Stopping the bleeding does not decrease the nurse's primary risk of infection.
2. An HIV test will not reveal the presence of HIV virus until weeks or months after infection.
3. Bandaging will only protect the wound from further infection, but not from possible organisms introduced by the needle-stick.
4. Hepatitis B virus vaccination after a needle-stick injury is recommended by infection disease protocols.

CLASSIFICATION

Competency Category:	Implementation
Taxonomic Level:	Application
Client Age:	Adult
Nursing Practice:	Clinical Techniques

REFERENCES
Kozier et al. (1991) p. 1308
Phipps et al. (1991) pp. 2287-2288

CASE 22

106 CORRECT ANSWER: 1

1. The oliguric phase of acute renal failure can include congestive heart failure.
2. Hypovolemia is a finding in the diuretic phase of acute renal failure.
3. Postural hypotension is a manifestation possible in the diuretic phase of acute renal failure.
4. Clients in the oliguric phase of acute renal failure are prone to fluid volume excess, not deficit.

CLASSIFICATION

Competency Category:	Analysis & Interpretation of Data
Taxonomic Level:	Critical Thinking
Client Age:	Older Adult
Nursing Practice:	Screening & Diagnosis

REFERENCES
Phipps et al. (1991), p. 1463
Smeltzer & Bare (1992), p. 673

107 CORRECT ANSWER: 3

1. Clients in the oliguric phase are on fluid restrictions and most are not able to tolerate oral feedings.
2. Clients only need to be weighed daily.
3. The side rails should be left up for safety reasons because drowsiness is a symptom of acute renal failure.
4. Strict bed rest is recommended during the oliguric phase of acute renal failure.

CLASSIFICATION

Competency Category:	Planning Care
Taxonomic Level:	Knowledge/Comprehension
Client Age:	Older Adult
Nursing Practice:	Physiological Needs

REFERENCES
Phipps et al. (1991), pp. 1465-1466
Smeltzer & Bare (1992), p. 674

108 CORRECT ANSWER: 2

1. It is important to turn and position these clients because they are prone to skin breakdown; however, it is not necessary to do this q. 1h.
2. Urinary output is crucial in the management of acute renal failure. All observations of the client's state of hydration need to be recorded so that hour-to-hour and day-to-day comparisons can be made.
3. It is important to do deep breathing exercises as these clients can progress to CHF; however, it is not necessary to do this q. 1h.
4. Edema may be present but it is not necessary to assess q. 1h.

CLASSIFICATION

Competency Category:	Implementation
Taxonomic Level:	Application
Client Age:	Older Adult
Nursing Practice:	Physiological Needs

REFERENCES
Phipps et al. (1991), p. 1465
Smeltzer & Bare (1992), p. 673

109   CORRECT ANSWER: 3

1. This response is inappropriate because the nurse should not leave an apprehensive client who is hemorrhaging.
2. This response is inappropriate because the nurse is suggesting the client is at fault, without addressing the client's apprehension.
3. This is the most appropriate response because the nurse is responding to the client's feelings and shows support in a calm manner.
4. This response is inappropriate because it does not take Mrs. Perry's anxiety into account.

CLASSIFICATION

Competency Category:	Implementation
Taxonomic Level:	Application
Client Age:	Older Adult
Nursing Practice:	Communication

REFERENCES
Johnson (1993), pp. 72-73
Smith (1992), p. 348

110   CORRECT ANSWER: 3

1. Changes should be reported immediately. Charting may not be done until late in the shift.
2. Rechecking the float nurse's assessment is an inappropriate use of the charge nurse's time.
3. Reviewing with the float nurse what should be assessed and reported is important because it ensures that the float nurse will assess and report relevant observations immediately.
4. Asking the nurse working in the next room to be available to the float nurse will not ensure that the float nurse will assess and report relevant observations immediately.

CLASSIFICATION

Competency Category:	Collaboration & Coordination
Taxonomic Level:	Knowledge/Comprehension
Client Age:	Older Adult
Nursing Practice:	Professional Responsibilities

REFERENCES
Craven & Hirnle (1992), pp. 18-19
Potter & Perry (1993), p. 211

111   CORRECT ANSWER: 3

1. Providing milkshakes t.i.d. is inappropriate because clients in acute renal failure should eat a low-protein, high-carbohydrate, high-fat diet. Milkshakes are high in protein and are, therefore, contraindicated.
2. Ensuring her privacy during meals is inappropriate because people tend to eat better in a social group setting than by themselves.
3. Appetite is often best in the morning and deteriorates gradually throughout the day. Therefore, a high-calorie breakfast should be encouraged.
4. Water between meals would ensure fluid intake, but would not provide the required calories.

CLASSIFICATION

Competency Category:	Implementation
Taxonomic Level:	Critical Thinking
Client Age:	Older Adult
Nursing Practice:	Physiological Needs

REFERENCES
Dudek (1993), pp. 340, 589
Phipps et al. (1991), p. 1469

CASE 23

112 CORRECT ANSWER: 1

1. Appropriate nursing interventions for an unconscious client include talking with the client while providing nursing care, explaining procedures, and identifying who is in the room.
2. The nurse should not discuss Paul's condition by talking "over" him. The nurse should assume that Paul can hear all conversations in his presence.
3. There is no special need to speak slowly or clearly to an unconscious client. It is inappropriate to use the family to pressure the client to perform activities.
4. Hearing is the last sensation lost with unconscious clients. Tactile stimulation is also important, but not at the expense of auditory stimulation; hence, whispering is an inappropriate approach.

CLASSIFICATION

Competency Category:	Implementation
Taxonomic Level:	Application
Client Age:	Child & Adolescent
Nursing Practice:	Communication

REFERENCES
Phipps et al. (1991), pp. 1761-1762
Potter & Perry (1993), pp. 339-340

113 CORRECT ANSWER: 3

1. Taping the hole contravenes principles of asepsis.
2. The high concentration of glucose in the amino acid solution stimulates high levels of insulin production. Suddenly removing the glucose source can precipitate a dangerous hypoglycemic reaction.
3. Infusing Dextrose 10% is the most appropriate action since it temporarily replaces the glucose source during the time the nurse awaits the delivery of the new bag.
4. The lipids would be an inappropriate replacement for the glucose and it would be incorrect to increase the rate of lipids being infused without a physician's order.

CLASSIFICATION

Competency Category:	Implementation
Taxonomic Level:	Critical Thinking
Client Age:	Child & Adolescent
Nursing Practice:	Clinical Techniques

REFERENCES
Black & Matassarin-Jabocs (1993), p. 1601
Ignatavicius & Bayne (1991), p. 324

114 CORRECT ANSWER: 2

1. Resting splints prevent contracture deformity (foot drop), but do not promote circulation.
2. Contracting and relaxing the leg muscles, even through passive means, promotes circulation in the lower extremities.
3. Administering warm packs to the calves is not an effective or safe measure to promote circulation.
4. Elevating the foot of the client's bed decreases arterial flow.

CLASSIFICATION

Competency Category:	Implementation
Taxonomic Level:	Application
Client Age:	Child & Adolescent
Nursing Practice:	Physiological Needs

REFERENCES

Black & Matassarin-Jabocs (1993), p. 1307
Craven & Hirnle (1992), p. 710

115 CORRECT ANSWER: 2

1. Good lighting is essential to assess the oxygen status of a ventilated client; therefore, lights should not be dimmed.
2. Linen that is wrinkle-free prevents skin breakdown, which is a risk for the unconscious client.
3. A prone position is not safe practice for a spinal cord injured, unconscious client because of the risk of aspiration.
4. Although Paul is unconscious, his privacy should still be maintained during personal care.

CLASSIFICATION

Competency Category:	Implementation
Taxonomic Level:	Application
Client Age:	Child & Adolescent
Nursing Practice:	Physiological Needs

REFERENCES

Black & Matassarin-Jabocs (1993), pp. 800-803
Phipps et al. (1991), pp. 1764-1765

116 CORRECT ANSWER: 2

1. Documenting this situation does not have any direct effect on promoting a safe practice environment.
2. Advising the nursing supervisor is the best means to promote a safe practice environment. It notifies the nurse administrator of the changing conditions on the unit and also sets in motion a plan for getting more help.
3. It would be inappropriate to leave the bedside of the unstable client for an extended period.
4. It would be inappropriate for the practical nurse/nursing assistant to provide care for a client who is not stable.

CLASSIFICATION

Competency Category:	Professional Practice
Taxonomic Level:	Critical Thinking
Client Age:	Child & Adolescent
Nursing Practice:	Professional Responsibilities

REFERENCES

Canadian Nurses Association (1991), p. 17
Yeo (1991), p. 191

117 CORRECT ANSWER: 3

1. Requesting a vacation does not address the underlying issues this nurse is facing. It is likely a means of temporary resolution.
2. Applying for a transfer to a less demanding unit would not address the underlying feelings the nurse is experiencing.
3. In approaching colleagues, the nurse is verbalizing and reflecting upon the feelings. The nurse is seeking a supportive, professional environment, and is recognizing that the feelings need resolution.
4. Considering the feelings as normal may result in developing unhealthy or detrimental coping mechanisms, which do not deal with the identified problem.

CLASSIFICATION

Competency Category:	Professional Practice
Taxonomic Level:	Critical Thinking
Client Age:	Child & Adolescent
Nursing Practice:	Professional Responsibilities

REFERENCES
Arnold & Boggs (1989), pp. 379-380
McClosky & Grace (1990), pp. 492-494

INDEPENDENT ITEMS

118 CORRECT ANSWER: 4

1. Asking if the pills upset her stomach does not assess the client's knowledge about self-management.
2. Determining what home remedies she uses does not support the diagnosis of a knowledge deficit.
3. Exploring the client's need for follow-up does not address the issue of her knowledge deficit or self-management. This option does not validate what the nurse has identified.
4. By assessing Mabel's understanding of her medications, the nurse is validating the presence or absence of a knowledge deficit.

CLASSIFICATION

Competency Category:	Analysis & Interpretation of Data
Taxonomic Level:	Application
Client Age:	Older Adult
Nursing Practice:	Communication

REFERENCES
Craven & Hirnle (1992), p. 120
Eliopoulos (1993), p. 164

119 CORRECT ANSWER: 4

1. The nurse's response in defending the charting is straightforward and assertive; however, it does not acknowledge any receptiveness to changes in charting.
2. Questioning the supervisor about the criticism is an example of seeking clarification. Although an appropriate communication technique, this does not address the nurse's receptiveness to change.
3. Responding with appreciation for the feedback given is polite, and shows respect for the nursing supervisor, but does not address the problem of charting, or show any willingness to change.
4. Giving thanks for the appraisal acknowledges the feedback from the nursing supervisor. The nurse maintains an assertive stance and asks for specific suggestions on how changes could be made.

CLASSIFICATION

Competency Category:	Professional Practice
Taxonomic Level:	Affective
Client Age:	General
Nursing Practice:	Professional Responsibilities

REFERENCES
Arnold & Boggs (1989), pp. 228-229, 360-365
Potter & Perry (1993), pp. 389-391

120 CORRECT ANSWER: 2

1. For a leg bag to be effective, the client must be in a sitting or standing position.
2. The drainage bag hanging over the end of the stretcher means it is below the level of the bladder. Gravity is used to assist drainage and decrease the possibility of backflow and subsequent infection.
3. Attaching the drainage bag and tubing to the siderails is unsafe and could result in injury to the client when the siderails are moved up or down.
4. With the bag and tubing between the client's legs, the entire system is horizontal and reflux is likely.

CLASSIFICATION

Competency Category:	Implementation
Taxonomic Level:	Application
Client Age:	General
Nursing Practice:	Clinical Techniques

REFERENCES
Kozier et al. (1991), p. 1219
Potter & Perry (1993), pp. 1370-1371

121 CORRECT ANSWER: 3

1. Informing the client may jeopardize the nurse-client relationship and increase the client's anxiety.
2. Reporting to the Director of Nursing is not the appropriate line of communication. The nurse has an obligation to speak directly with the colleague first. If the response is not appropriate, the nurse can then go to the next authority, the nursing supervisor.
3. Discussing the situation with the colleague immediately is the recommended practice, provided the situation can be resolved without risk to present or future clients.
4. The situation must be dealt with immediately to avoid undue risk to other clients.

CLASSIFICATION

Competency Category:	Professional Practice
Taxonomic Level:	Application
Client Age:	General
Nursing Practice:	Professional Responsibilities

REFERENCES

Canadian Nurses Association (1991), pp. 15-16

Potter & Perry (1993), p. 276

122 CORRECT ANSWER: 4

1. Asking the client about influenza vaccination demonstrates a lack of awareness for the client's message and feelings.
2. Telling the client everyone has a cold provides only superficial acknowledgement of the client's message, and minimizes the client's feelings.
3. Suggesting to the client that he is afraid the cold will become pneumonia jumps to a conclusion and suggests what his concern might be.
4. Repeating the client's statement that he is concerned about having a cold for more than a week acknowledges the client's message and feelings. This statement demonstrates reflection, which is a technique for therapeutic communication.

CLASSIFICATION

Competency Category:	Implementation
Taxonomic Level:	Application
Client Age:	Older Adult
Nursing Practice:	Communication

REFERENCES

Arnold & Boggs (1989), pp. 182-184

Smith (1992), pp. 93-115

123 CORRECT ANSWER: 2

1. Following cleansing and prior to suturing, the laceration should be covered with a sterile (or clean) dressing to prevent infection.
2. The wound will require a thorough cleansing and removal of foreign material prior to suturing to prevent infectious process. Covering the injury with a sterile dressing will decrease the likelihood of infection.
3. For maximum healing, suturing should be carried out within the first few hours after the injury.
4. Clotting should occur in a few minutes, and suturing should take place within a few hours of the injury.

CLASSIFICATION

Competency Category:	Implementation
Taxonomic Level:	Application
Client Age:	Child & Adolescent
Nursing Practice:	Clinical Techniques

REFERENCES

Phipps et al. (1991), pp. 2288-2289
Potter & Perry (1993), p. 1661

124 CORRECT ANSWER: 3

1. Not all clients with herpes have recurrences, and the number of recurrences cannot be predicted.
2. There are long-term effects (e.g., increased risk of cervical cancer; risk of neonatal transmission during labor/delivery).
3. The nurse is being honest and sincere in providing the information. There is an increased risk of cervical cancer and, because the virus is harbored in nerve endings, neonatal transmission during labor/delivery is possible.
4. The nurse is not answering the client's question.

CLASSIFICATION

Competency Category:	Professional Practice
Taxonomic Level:	Critical Thinking
Client Age:	Child & Adolescent
Nursing Practice:	Psychosocial Needs

REFERENCES

Ignatavicius & Bayne (1991), p. 1780
Olds et al. (1992), p. 222

125 CORRECT ANSWER: 3

1. Bringing in favorite snacking foods does not demonstrate an understanding that Mary Anne must change her behavior.
2. Planning a birthday party does not demonstrate an understanding of the principles of behavior modification.
3. Accepting the decision to withdraw visiting privileges demonstrates that the family understands the principle of earning privileges for acceptable behavior and losing privileges for unacceptable behavior.
4. Indicating that negative reinforcement should come only from the nursing staff does not demonstrate support of Mary Anne. Family cooperation in the negative reinforcement aspect of therapy is necessary.

CLASSIFICATION

Competency Category:	Evaluation
Taxonomic Level:	Critical Thinking
Client Age:	Child & Adolescent
Nursing Practice:	Psychosocial Needs

REFERENCES

Haber & McMahon (1992), p. 331
Wilson & Kneisl (1992), pp. 761-765

126 CORRECT ANSWER: 1

1. If the tips of wet forceps are held up, the water will travel down the forceps to the handle, which is considered contaminated. If the forceps are then tipped downward again, pathogens will travel to and contaminate the sterile forcep tips.
2. The incision should be cleansed from "clean-to-dirty."
3. It is usually unnecessary to wear gloves and a mask to do a dressing change. If there is drainage, gloves might be appropriate.
4. There is a 2.5 cm border at the periphery of the sterile field which is not considered sterile. To avoid contamination, sterile items should not be placed in this area.

CLASSIFICATION

Competency Category:	Implementation
Taxonomic Level:	Application
Client Age:	General
Nursing Practice:	Clinical Techniques

REFERENCES

Kozier et al. (1991), pp. 478, 1323
Taylor et al. (1993), pp. 518, 1281-1283

127 CORRECT ANSWER: 4

1. It is misleading to suggest to a child that changes will not be necessary. She will need to attain new knowledge, skills, and attitudes to deal with this chronic health condition.
2. Contemporary diabetic diets are flexible.
3. It is important that the child with diabetes continue to be involved in normal childhood activities.
4. The goal of diabetes therapy should be to achieve normal blood glucose levels. Therefore, she will need to learn new skills related to diet, exercise, and medication.

CLASSIFICATION

Competency Category:	Planning Care
Taxonomic Level:	Application
Client Age:	Child & Adolescent
Nursing Practice:	Psychosocial Needs

REFERENCES
Guthrie & Guthrie (1991), pp. 53-58
Mott et al. (1990), pp. 1519-1529

128 CORRECT ANSWER: 3

1. Because of Rita's unpredictable behavior, isolation may provide an opportunity for the client to harm herself.
2. Rita is too ill to respond constructively to being confronted by the nurse.
3. Frequent observation is the most effective means of monitoring unpredictable behavior; it acknowledges risks and promotes a safe environment.
4. A structured social activity requires too much focus and concentration for a client in this state.

CLASSIFICATION

Competency Category:	Implementation
Taxonomic Level:	Application
Client Age:	Adult
Nursing Practice:	Physiological Needs

REFERENCES
Potter & Perry (1993), pp. 896-897
Wilson & Kneisl (1992), p. 301

129 CORRECT ANSWER: 2

1. Providing feedback to him will not assist in controlling his behavior.
2. The client needs external controls until he is able to set limits on his own physical activity. A structured, subdued environment decreases stimulation, which would help to decrease restlessness and hyperactivity.
3. Close supervision of medication administration is only necessary if the nurse suspects a client is not swallowing the prescribed medication.
4. Encouraging singing and joke telling only escalates this behavior, exhausts the client, and is of little therapeutic value.

CLASSIFICATION

Competency Category:	Implementation
Taxonomic Level:	Application
Client Age:	Child & Adolescent
Nursing Practice:	Psychosocial Needs

REFERENCES
Beck et al. (1993), pp. 275-277
Stuart & Sundeen (1991), pp. 443-454

APPENDICES

ABC

APPENDIX A: THE RN EXAM LIST OF COMPETENCIES (BY GROUP)

GROUP A: **71 COMPETENCIES**

50–65% of the RN Exam

GROUP B: **68 COMPETENCIES**

20–35% of the RN Exam

GROUP C: **50 COMPETENCIES**

5–15% of the RN Exam

GROUP D: **49 COMPETENCIES**

1–10% of the RN Exam

GROUP A

DATA COLLECTION

The nurse...

- establishes a professional relationship with the client during the initial nursing history (e.g., identifies self by name and role; answers client's questions; provides information concerning the physical environment, expected routines, and services offered by the facility; interprets the nursing role with respect to availability, approachability, responsibility and limitations).

- uses appropriate sources for data collection: the client.

- uses appropriate sources for data collection: knowledge from nursing, in related fields and disciplines.

- selects data collection techniques pertinent to the client and the situation (e.g., observation; auscultation; palpation; percussion; inspection; selected screening tests; interview; consultation; measuring and monitoring).

- conducts an interview with the client using the principles of communication (e.g., listens actively; structures the interview in such a way as to obtain the necessary data).

- collects client-related biophysiological data, through observation and interview, for initial and ongoing nursing assessments (e.g., vital signs; circulatory and respiratory status; lifestyle factors such as sleep and exercise; sensory deficits in hearing, vision and extremities; level of consciousness).

- collects client-related psychosocial data, through observation and interview, for initial and ongoing nursing assessments (e.g., cultural values, beliefs and customs related to health situation; developmental tasks; spiritual beliefs; family history; perception of present health situation).

- modifies the assessment phase to suit the client's health situation.

- records the data collected.

ANALYSIS AND INTERPRETATION OF DATA

The nurse...

- analyzes data by determining a relationship among the various data collected (e.g., determines a relationship between the client's color, blood gas report and verbalization of dyspnea).

- interprets data based on scientific knowledge and norms (e.g., takes the analyzed data and determines that the client's color, blood gas report and statement of dyspnea are not normal and that a problem exists with the respiratory system).

- interprets data taking into account the plan of care established by the health care team.

- formulates nursing diagnoses which identify actual or potential health problems.

PLANNING CARE

The nurse...

- facilitates the client's participation in the planning of care (e.g., fosters an environment that allows for questioning, exchange of information, and a creative approach to care).

- plans nursing interventions which are compatible with the client's existing resources.

- develops the plan of care by: prioritizing client needs.

- develops the plan of care by: establishing expected outcomes for the client.

- develops the plan of care by: identifying nursing interventions.

- develops the plan of care by: prioritizing nursing interventions.

- documents the plan of care.

IMPLEMENTATION

The nurse...

- implements nursing interventions using agency policies and protocols, principles of safety and appropriate resources (e.g., providing support to the client during procedures).

- helps the client to understand the interventions and their relationship to expected outcomes (e.g., possible risk, discomforts, inconveniences, costs).

- modifies interventions to suit the client's situation by: selecting interventions that are consistent with the priority of the health situation.

- modifies interventions to suit the client's situation by: selecting interventions that are consistent with the client's identified concerns and priorities.

- modifies interventions to suit the client's situation by: considering the client's tolerance when sequencing interventions.

- modifies interventions to suit the client's situation by: providing immediate interventions for urgent health situations.

- documents interventions by: using a concise and organized manner.

- documents interventions by: recording them as soon as possible, without compromising client safety.

- documents interventions by: identifying those which are pertinent to the client's situation.

- provides nursing interventions which assist the client to meet altered food and fluid needs by maintaining established peripheral intravenous therapy.

- promotes comfort and pain management by: medicating.

- gives the medication while applying the following principles: demonstrating knowledge of medications.

- gives the medication while applying the following principles: calculating dosage correctly.

- gives the medication while applying the following principles: determining dosage is safe.

- gives the medication while applying the following principles: preparing drug appropriately.

- gives the medication while applying the following principles: administering medication on time.

- gives the medication while applying the following principles: observing for desired effects.

- gives the medication while applying the following principles: observing for side effects.

- gives the medication while applying the following principles: observing for interactions.

- gives the medication while applying the following principles: justifying the administration of a p.r.n. medication.

- gives the medication while applying the following principles: assessing client's perception of the response to medication.

- promotes a safe environment by: correcting factors that are detrimental to the psychological safety of the client.

- uses principles of a helping relationship when providing nursing care by: demonstrating a helping attitude (e.g., empathy, warmth, respect).

• uses principles of a helping relationship when providing nursing care by: using therapeutic communication techniques (e.g., reflection, clarification, summarizing).

• uses principles of a helping relationship when providing nursing care by: identifying communication barriers.

• promotes acceptance of sexuality by: demonstrating non-judgmental behavior.

• prepares the client for laboratory investigation, diagnostic examinations and treatments using agency policies and procedures, principles of safety and appropriate resources (e.g., explaining laboratory tests, diagnostic examinations and treatments to the client; explaining normal or therapeutic values to the client; obtaining specimens from the client).

• intervenes in response to changes observed in the client's condition by: immediately intervening.

• intervenes in response to changes observed in the client's condition by: intervening according to protocol.

• acknowledges mourning by family members of a deceased client (e.g., offers privacy for them to talk and grieve; explains the compulsory procedures they must go through; ensures that all family members are in a condition to leave the hospital).

• plans for discharge by: anticipating client's health care needs on return to the community.

• plans for discharge by: verifying that the client is able to meet health care needs on discharge (e.g., medication administration, dietary alterations, self-care activities, resource utilization).

EVALUATION

The nurse observes changes in the client's condition, on an ongoing basis.

COLLABORATION AND COORDINATION

The nurse acts as a health care team member by: establishing and maintaining effective communication with the health care team.

PROFESSIONAL PRACTICE

The nurse...

• practices within the provisions governing practice: nurses act and standards of practice.

• practices within the provisions governing practice: code of ethics.

• practices within the provisions governing practice: regulations/bylaws respecting nursing acts.

• acts as a client advocate within the health care team by: assisting the client to gain access to quality health care in such a way as to maintain the client's health, safety and integrity.

• acts as a client advocate within the health care team by: facilitating, ensuring, and monitoring the quality of care received by the client.

• acts as a client advocate within the health care team by: challenging questionable orders and decisions by medical and professional staff.

• acts as a client advocate within the health care team by: protecting individual rights to confidentiality, privacy, beliefs, values.

• acts as a client advocate within the health care team by: reporting incidents of unsafe nursing practice to the appropriate authority.

• acts as a client advocate within the health care team by: reporting unsafe practices of other members of the health team to the appropriate persons.

• assesses self in terms of: performance as a care provider.

- assesses self in terms of: knowledge/experience required to improve practice and promote professional growth.

- exercises judgment when performing agency procedures and job requirements.

- is accountable for own actions.

- assumes responsibility for nursing care, even when assigned to others.

- evaluates own workload, and identifies an unrealistic workload for self.

- having identified an unrealistic workload, asks for assistance if necessary.

- demonstrates behavior consistent with the professional role by accepting constructive feedback from colleagues.

GROUP B

DATA COLLECTION

The nurse uses appropriate sources for data collection: previous and current health records/nursing care plans.

ANALYSIS AND INTERPRETATION OF DATA

The nurse validates the interpretation of the data with other members of the health care team as required.

PLANNING CARE

N/A.

IMPLEMENTATION

The nurse...

- promotes ventilation and respiration by: performing cardiopulmonary resuscitation.

- promotes ventilation and respiration by: performing oral or nasal suctioning.

- promotes ventilation and respiration by: administering oxygen.

- promotes ventilation and respiration by: assisting client with deep breathing and coughing.

- promotes ventilation and respiration by: proper positioning.

- promotes circulation by: controlling bleeding.

- promotes circulation by: assisting the client with active and passive exercises.

- provides nursing interventions which assist the client to meet altered food and fluid needs by: promoting adequate oral fluid intake.

- provides nursing interventions which assist the client to meet altered food and fluid needs by: discontinuing intravenous therapy.

- provides nursing interventions which assist the client to meet altered food and fluid needs by: administering/maintaining blood transfusion.

- provides nursing interventions which assist the client to meet altered food and fluid needs by: recording intake.

- promotes elimination by: caring for drainage tubes and collection devices.

- promotes elimination by: performing bladder catheterization.

- promotes elimination by: measuring output.

- promotes comfort and pain management by: positioning.

- gives the medication while applying the following principles: checking the chart for the original order.

- gives the medication while applying the following principles: identifying correct medication.

- gives the medication while applying the following principles: identifying client.

- gives the medication while applying the following principles: using appropriate administration technique.

- gives the medication while applying the following principles: recording medication appropriately.

- gives the medication while applying the following principles: documenting client's response to medication.

- promotes balance between rest/sleep and activity by: encouraging exercise and ambulation.

- promotes body alignment by: proper positioning.

- promotes hygiene by: assisting client to bathe or bathing client.

- promotes hygiene by: assisting with other aspects of personal hygiene (e.g., mouth care, foot care, perineal care).

- promotes tissue integrity by: providing skin care (e.g., washing, drying, positioning).

- promotes tissue integrity by: providing wound care (e.g., cleansing, dressing).

- prevents infection by: implementing established protocol for reporting.

- prevents infection by: practicing surgical asepsis.

- prevents infection by: practicing isolation techniques.

- prevents infection by: using universal precautions.

- promotes sensory stimulation by: talking with the client during nursing care.

- promotes a safe environment by: monitoring factors that are detrimental to the physical safety of the client (e.g., wet floors, inadequate lighting).

- promotes a safe environment by: monitoring factors that are detrimental to the psychological safety of the client (e.g., lack of privacy; sensory overload; too heavy or too limited schedules).

- promotes a safe environment by: correcting factors that are detrimental to the physical safety of the client.

- promotes a safe environment by: ensuring mechanical equipment/safety.

- promotes a safe environment by: recognizing risks for incidents and accidents.

- promotes a safe environment by: supervising the activities of clients who are at risk.

- promotes a safe environment by: utilizing safety measures to protect self from injury.

- promotes a safe environment by: taking the necessary precautions to prevent accident's, according to the client's condition (e.g., bed rails; accessibility of the call bell; being present when a client is agitated, when the client is transferred to the examination table or is brought to the operating room; for transfers).

- uses principles of a helping relationship when providing nursing care by: using other means to communicate when barriers exist (e.g., interpreter, touch, gestures).

- uses principles of a helping relationship when providing nursing care by: using appropriate means to communicate with an unconscious client (e.g., talks to client, uses sensory stimulation that is familiar to client).

- uses teaching/learning principles to facilitate client/family learning by: using terminology appropriate for the client/family.

EVALUATION

The nurse...

- ensures that the client has received the planned care (e.g., verification with the client, with the staff, in the written documents).

- informs appropriate health team members of significant changes in the client's condition.

- revises the plan of care as indicated.

- evaluates nursing care by: verifying the client's progress toward the expected outcomes.

COLLABORATION AND COORDINATION

The nurse...

- informs nursing staff of pertinent information related to nursing care (e.g., changes made in the care plan, changes in the client's behavior).

- requests that the nursing staff report any noticeable changes in the client's condition.

PROFESSIONAL PRACTICE

The nurse...

- discovering that, when a client refuses a prescribed treatment, tries to find out the reason for the refusal.

- discovering that a client refuses a prescribed treatment, after discussing it with the client, refers the problem to the professional concerned if treatment is essential.

- discovering that a client refuses a prescribed treatment, records the refusal in the chart.

- asks help and guidance when unable to perform competently.

- questions the appropriate person when agency policies, procedures, and job requirements are considered inappropriate.

- refrains from practicing beyond competence.

- uses means to update competence (e.g., reading; courses; study days; conferences; fieldwork experience).

- demonstrates use of new nursing knowledge in practice.

- demonstrates an attitude of inquiry to enhance nursing practice.

- demonstrates respect for nursing colleagues.

- demonstrates a commitment to the profession of nursing.

- demonstrates behavior consistent with the professional role by: being receptive to change.

- demonstrates behavior consistent with the professional role by: being open to new ideas.

- demonstrates behavior consistent with the professional role by: being honest/sincere.

- demonstrates behavior consistent with the professional role by: practicing confidentiality.

- demonstrates behavior consistent with the professional role by: maintaining clients' privacy.

- demonstrates a caring attitude as the foundation for nursing practice.

GROUP C

DATA COLLECTION

The nurse...

- uses appropriate sources for data collection: family members/significant persons.

- uses scientific principles related to the data collection techniques used.

- validates the data with the client/family.

ANALYSIS AND INTERPRETATION OF DATA

The nurse...

- validates her interpretation of the data with the client/family.

- formulates nursing diagnoses which identify areas for health promotion.

- validates the nursing diagnoses with the client/family.

- validates the nursing diagnoses with the nursing team.

PLANNING CARE

The nurse...

- discusses with the client* the health care outcomes in regard to the health problem or nursing diagnoses.

- develops the plan of care by: establishing target dates.

---

* Significant persons might be included in these discussions depending on the client's wish.

- develops the plan of care by: identifying required resources.

- consults with members of the health care team in planning care.

- provides the rationale for the plan of care.

IMPLEMENTATION

The nurse...

- encourages the client/family to participate in the implementation of care (e.g., administration of insulin, intermittent catheterization).

- provides nursing interventions which assist the client to meet altered food and fluid needs by: maintaining total parenteral nutrition infusion.

- provides nursing interventions which assist the client to meet altered food and fluid needs by: maintaining established central venous intravenous therapy.

- promotes the client's positive self-concept by: facilitating client's integration of changes in body image.

- promotes the client's positive self-concept by: promoting use of effective coping techniques to deal with expected and unexpected life events (e.g., loss).

- promotes the client's positive self-concept by: supporting cultural and spiritual preferences.

- uses teaching/learning principles to facilitate client/family learning by: assessing learning needs.

- uses teaching/learning principles to facilitate client/family learning by: assessing readiness to learn.

- uses teaching/learning principles to facilitate client/family learning by: identifying strategies to facilitate change.

- uses teaching/learning principles to facilitate client/family learning by: validating learning objectives with client/family.

- uses teaching/learning principles to facilitate client/family learning by: implementing a teaching plan.

- uses teaching/learning principles to facilitate client/family learning by: using a variety of opportunities for teaching.

- uses teaching/learning principles to facilitate client/family learning by: creating an environment conducive to learning.

- uses teaching/learning principles to facilitate client/family learning by: using existing resources to support teaching.

- uses teaching/learning principles to facilitate client/family learning by: building on previous experience/education.

- uses teaching/learning principles to facilitate client/family learning by: evaluating the effectiveness of the teaching plan.

- identifies a rapidly changing health situation (e.g., clarifying the problem with the client; determining what the client can do in such a situation; verifying what the client expects of the nurse/support system; suggesting possible solutions; offering the client the necessary support in order to successfully deal with the situation).

- intervenes in response to changes observed in the client's condition by: maintaining an efficient manner.

- applies the basic principles of rehabilitation (e.g., the beginning is initiated early; the process is gradual; the client's tolerance is respected; the client's improvements are pointed out even if they are minimal).

- plans for discharge by: initiating strategies to maintain continuity of care on discharge (e.g., teaching, referral, family consultation).

- plans for discharge by: validating the client's needs for return to the community.

- plans for discharge by: assisting the client in accessing community resources.

EVALUATION

The nurse evaluates nursing care by: validating the client's perception of their progress toward the expected outcomes.

COLLABORATION AND COORDINATION

The nurse...

- assigns health care activities to allied nursing personnel consistent with levels of expertise, education, job description, and client needs.

- provides rationale for the assignment of nursing activities based on client needs, nursing staff competence, nursing staff duties.

- coordinates the care plan to be implemented by other members of the nursing staff.

- acts as a health care team member by: presenting the client's perspective.

- acts as a health care team member by: coordinating with the client and other professionals the activities provided for in the therapeutic plan in order to ensure continuity.

- demonstrates leadership skills within the nursing team (e.g., team leader).

- recognizes the components of effective group structure and functioning.

- demonstrates team building skills that promote collegial relationships within the health care team.

PROFESSIONAL PRACTICE

The nurse...

• acts as a client advocate within the health care team by: ensuring appropriate and timely responses by health team members.

• discovering that a client refuses a prescribed treatment, accepts the client's decision.

• utilizes responsible practices which contribute to cost-effective use of health care resources.

• identifies and responds to professional, legal, and ethical issues that arise.

• promotes change, utilizing knowledge of formal and informal power structure and appropriate channels of communication.

• participates in planning changes that lead to improvement in the work setting.

• provides constructive feedback to colleagues.

GROUP D

DATA COLLECTION

The nurse...

• uses appropriate sources for data collection: other professionals/facilities/agencies.

• collects client-related environmental data, through observation and interview, for initial and ongoing nursing assessments (e.g., housing; work environment; urban or rural community).

• validates the data with other members of the health care team.

ANALYSIS AND INTERPRETATION OF DATA

N/A.

PLANNING CARE

The nurse describes steps in planning nursing care.

IMPLEMENTATION

The nurse...

• promotes ventilation and respiration by: using oropharyngeal airway and resuscitation bag.

• provides nursing interventions which assist the client to meet altered food and fluid needs by: assisting with menu/meal planning.

• provides nursing interventions which assist the client to meet altered food and fluid needs by: assisting with oral feeding.

• provides nursing interventions which assist the client to meet altered food and fluid needs by: inserting and removing nasogastric tubes.

• provides nursing interventions which assist the client to meet altered food and fluid needs by: performing gastric feeding via gastrotomy/nasogastric tube.

• provides nursing interventions which assist the client to meet altered food and fluid needs by: maintaining heparin/saline lock.

• promotes elimination by: using and teaching routines and dietary control.

• promotes elimination by: providing ostomy care.

• promotes elimination by: administering enemas and suppositories.

- promotes elimination by: disimpacting.

- promotes elimination by: irrigating bladder.

- promotes comfort and pain management by: applying heat and cold.

- promotes comfort and pain management by: using touch, massage, and stress reduction techniques.

- promotes comfort and pain management by: ensuring proper maintenance of orthesis and prosthesis.

- promotes balance between rest/sleep and activity by: pacing routines and activities.

- promotes balance between rest/sleep and activity by: facilitating diversional activity.

- promotes balance between rest/sleep and activity by: assisting the client with mobilizing devices.

- promotes balance between rest/sleep and activity by: using and teaching relaxation techniques.

- promotes body alignment by: caring for the client with external immobilizing devices.

- promotes sensory stimulation by: preventing overload of sensory stimulation (e.g., mechanical noise, lights).

- promotes sensory stimulation by: facilitating the presence of a significant person.

- promotes sensory stimulation by: touching the client when talking with them.

- promotes sensory stimulation by: using humor.

- promotes acceptance of sexuality by: teaching about safe sexual practices.

- promotes acceptance of sexuality by: promoting healthy sexuality.

- promotes acceptance of sexuality by: teaching about family planning.

- promotes the client's positive self-concept by: validating client's strengths.

- promotes social interaction of clients by: encouraging social participation.

- promotes social interaction of clients by: creating opportunities for social interaction.

- uses teaching/learning principles to facilitate client/family learning by: providing opportunities for client/family to practice new knowledge.

- with the client's consent, instructs family how they may participate in client care (e.g., hygiene, walking, stoma care, baby feeding).

- intervenes in response to changes observed in the client's condition by: intervening according to a standing order.

- justifies the choice of persons she notifies in an emergency situation (e.g., family, priest).

EVALUATION

The nurse evaluates nursing care by: determining the client's/family's satisfaction.

COLLABORATION AND COORDINATION

The nurse...

- describes the functions of the other categories of nursing staff.

- acts as a health care team member by: clarifying the nurses' role and responsibilities to other team members.

- acts as a health care team member by: contributing to the identification of health issue(s)/problems from the nursing perspective.

- acts as a health care team member by: sharing knowledge and expertise with others.

- acts as a health care team member by: referring problems to appropriate team members/agencies as necessary (e.g., seeking support in care the nurse cannot totally conduct—spiritual, nutritional).

- acts as a health care team member by: supporting the contribution of each member of the health care team.

PROFESSIONAL PRACTICE

The nurse...

- describes the independent and interdependent functions related to the role of the nurse.

- states the professional goals of nursing practice.

- recognizes the importance of research as a basis for nursing practice.

- incorporates relevant research findings in nursing practice.

- understands the function of the health care delivery system: within the province of licensure.

APPENDIX B: REGISTERING/LICENSING AUTHORITIES

To obtain information on writing the RN Exam, contact the registering/licensing authority for your province or territory.

Alberta Association of Registered Nurses
11620 – 168th Street
Edmonton, AB
T5M 4A6

    (403) 451-0043
Fax: (403) 452-3276

Northwest Territories Registered Nurses Association
P.O. Box 2757
Yellowknife, NT
X1A 2R1

    (403) 873-2745
Fax: (403) 873-2336

Saskatchewan Registered Nurses' Association
2066 Retallack Street
Regina, SK
S4T 7X5

    (306) 757-4643
Fax: (306) 525-0849

Manitoba Association of Registered Nurses
647 Broadway Avenue
Winnipeg, MB
R3C OX2

    (204) 774-3477
Fax: (204) 775-6052

Registered Nurses' Association of Nova Scotia
Suite 104
120 Eileen Stubbs Avenue
Dartmouth, NS
B3B 1Y1

    (902) 468-9744
Fax: (902) 468-9510

College of Nurses of Ontario
101 Davenport Road
Toronto, ON
M5R 3P1

    (416) 928-0900
Fax: (416) 928-6507

Registered Nurses Association of British Columbia
2855 Arbutus Street
Vancouver, BC
V6J 3Y8

    (604) 736-7331
Fax: (604) 738-2272

Association of Registered Nurses of Newfoundland
P.O. Box 6116
55 Military Road
St. John's, NF
A1C 5X8

    (709) 753-6040
Fax: (709) 753-4940

Order of Nurses of Québec
4200 ouest, boulevard Dorchester
Montréal, PQ
H3Z 1V4

    (514) 935-2501
Fax: (514) 935-1799

Association of Nurses of Prince Edward Island
17 Pownal Street
Charlottetown, PE
C1A 3V7

    (902) 368-3764
Fax: (902) 628-1430

Nurses Association of New Brunswick
165 Regent Street
Fredericton, NB
E3B 3W5

    (506) 458-8731
Fax: (506) 459-2838

Yukon Registered Nurses Association
Suite 14, 1114 – 1 Avenue
Whitehorse, YT
Y1A 1A3

    (403) 667-4062
Fax: (403) 668-5123

APPENDIX C: ABBREVIATIONS

The abbreviations used in the Practice Exam are defined as follows:

BP	blood pressure	mL	millilitre(s)
b.i.d.	twice daily	mmHg	millimetres of mercury
° C	degrees Celsius	min	minute(s)
cm	centimetre(s)	P	pulse
h	hour	p.o.	orally
I.M.	intramuscular	p.r.n.	as needed
I.V.	intravenous	q.i.d.	4 times daily
kg	kilogram(s)	q. 8h	every 8 hours
L	litre(s)	stat.	immediately
mEq	milliequivalent	T	temperature
mg	milligram(s)	t.i.d.	3 times daily

BIBLIOGRAPHY

BIBLIOGRAPHY

This bibliography contains the references used to produce the Practice Exam.

Arnold, E., & Boggs, K. U. (1989). *Interpersonal relationships: Professional communication skills for nurses.* Toronto: Saunders.

Baer, C. L., & Williams, B. R. (1992). *Clinical pharmacology and nursing* (2nd ed.). Springhouse, PA: Springhouse.

Baird, S. B., McCorkle, R., & Grant, M. (1991). *Cancer nursing: A comprehensive textbook.* Philadelphia: Saunders.

Baumgart, A. J. (1992). *Canadian nursing faces the future* (2nd ed.). Toronto: Mosby.

Beare, P. G., & Myers, J. L. (1990). *Principles and practice of adult health nursing.* Toronto: Mosby.

Beck, C. K., Rawlins, R. P., & Williams, S. R. (1993). *Mental health psychiatric nursing* (3rd ed.). Toronto: Mosby.

Beckingham, A. C., & DuGas, B. W. (1993). *Promoting healthy aging.* Toronto: Mosby.

Birchenall, J. M., & Streight, M. E. (1993). *Care of the older adult* (3rd ed.). Philadelphia: Lippincott.

Black, J. M., & Matassarin-Jacobs, E. (1993). *Luckmann and Sorenson's medical-surgical nursing: A psychophysiologic approach* (4th ed.). Philadelphia: Saunders.

Burke, M. M., & Walsh, M. B. (1992). *Gerontological nursing: Care of the frail elderly.* Toronto: Mosby Yearbook.

Burrell, L. O. (1992). *Adult nursing in hospital and community settings.* Norwalk, CT: Appleton & Lange.

Canadian Nurses Association. (1993). *Blueprint for the criterion-referenced nurse registration/licensure examination.* Ottawa: Author.

Canadian Nurses Association. (1991). *Code of ethics for nursing.* Ottawa: Author.

Canadian Pharmaceutical Association. (1994). *Compendium of pharmaceuticals and specialties* (29th ed.). Ottawa: Author.

Carnevali, D. L., & Patrick, M. (1993). *Nursing management for the elderly* (3rd ed.). Philadelphia: Lippincott.

Castiglia, P. T., & Harben, R. E. (1992). *Child health care: Process and practice.* Philadelphia: Lippincott.

Christensen, B., & Kockrow, E. (1991). *Foundations of nursing.* Toronto: Mosby.

Cohen, S. M., Kenner, C. A., & Hollingsworth, A. O. (1991). *Maternal, neonatal, and women's health nursing.* Springhouse, PA: Springhouse.

Craven, R. F., & Hirnle, C. J. (1992). *Fundamentals of nursing: Human health and function.* Philadelphia: Lippincott.

Dudek, S. G. (1993). *Nutrition handbook for nursing practice* (2nd ed.). Philadelphia: Lippincott.

Duff, D. L. (1992). *A metric guide for health professionals on dosages and solutions* (3rd ed.). Toronto: Saunders.

Durham, J. D., & Cohen, F. L. (1991). *The person with AIDS: Nursing perspectives* (2nd ed.). New York: Springer.

Ebersole, P., & Hess, P. (1990). *Toward healthy aging: Human needs and nursing reponse* (3rd ed.). Toronto: Mosby.

Eliopoulos, C. (1993). *Gerontological nursing* (3rd ed.). Philadelphia: Lippincott.

Ellis, J. R., & Hartley, C. L. (1992). *Nursing in today's world* (4th ed.). Philadelphia: Lippincott.

Flaskerud, J. H., & Ungvarski, P. J. (1992). *HIV/AIDS infection: A guide to nursing care* (2nd ed.). Philadelphia: Saunders.

Fogel, C. I., & Lauver, D. R. (1990). *Sexual health promotion*. Philadelphia: Saunders.

Foster, R. L., Hunsberger, M. M., & Anderson, J. J. (1989). *Family-centered nursing care of children*. Philadelphia: Saunders.

Shannon, M., & Wilson, B. A. (1992). *Govoni & Hayes: Drugs and nursing implications* (7th ed.). Norwalk, CT: Appleton & Lange.

Guthrie, D. W., & Guthrie, R. A. (1991). *Nursing management of diabetes mellitus* (3rd ed.). New York: Springer.

Haber, J., & McMahon, A. L. (1992). *Comprehensive psychiatric nursing* (4th ed.). St. Louis: Mosby.

Ignatavicius, D. D., & Bayne, M. V. (1991). *Medical-surgical nursing: A nursing process approach*. Philadelphia: Saunders.

Jackson, D. B., & Saunders, R. B. (1993). *Child health nursing: A comprehensive approach to the care of children and their families*. Philadelphia: Lippincott.

Johnson, B. S. (1993). *Adaptation & growth: Psychiatric mental health nursing* (3rd ed.). Philadelphia: Lippincott.

Kozier, B., Erb, G. L., & Olivieri, R. (1991). *Fundamentals of nursing: Concepts, process and practice* (4th ed.). Redwood City, CA: Addison-Wesley.

Lewis, S. M., & Collier, I. C. (1992). *Medical-surgical nursing: Assessment and management of clinical problems* (3rd ed.). Toronto: Mosby.

Loebl, S., Spratto, G. R., Woods, A. L., & Matejski, M. (1991). *The nurse's drug handbook* (6th ed.). New York: Delmar.

Malseed, R. T., & Girton, S. E. (1990). *Pharmacology: Drug therapy and nursing considerations* (3rd ed.). Philadelphia: Lippincott.

May, K. A., & Mahlmeister, L. R. (1990). *Comprehensive maternity nursing: Nursing process and the childbearing family* (2nd ed.). Philadelphia: Lippincott.

McCloskey, J. C., & Grace, H. K. (1990). *Current issues in nursing* (3rd ed.). Toronto: Mosby.

Morris, J. J. (1991). *Canadian nurses and the law*. Toronto: Butterworths.

Mott, S. R., James, S. R., & Sperhac, A. M. (1990). *Nursing care of children and families* (2nd ed.). Redwood City, CA: Addison-Wesley.

Olds, S. B., London, M. L., & Ladewig, P. A. (1992). *Maternal-newborn nursing: A family-centered approach.* (4th ed.). Menlo Park, CA: Addison-Wesley.

Otto, S. (1991). *Oncology nursing.* Toronto: Mosby.

Phipps, W. J., Long, B. C., Woods, N. F., & Cassmeyer, V. L. (1991). *Medical-surgical nursing: Concepts and clinical practice* (4th ed.). Toronto: Mosby.

Pillitteri, A. (1992). *Maternal and child health nursing: Care of the childbearing and childrearing family.* Philadelphia: Lippincott.

Potter, P. A., & Perry, A. G. (1993). *Fundamentals of nursing: Concepts, process and practice* (3rd ed.). Toronto: Mosby.

Potter, P. A., & Perry, A. G. (1993). *Basic nursing: Theory and practice* (3rd ed.). Toronto: Mosby.

Reeder, S. J., Martin, L. L., & Koniak, D. (1992). *Maternity nursing: Family, newborn, and women's health care* (17th ed.). Philadelphia: Lippincott.

Skidmore-Roth, L. (1993). *Mosby's 1993 nursing drug reference.* Toronto: Mosby.

Smeltzer, S. C., & Bare, B. G. (Eds.). (1992). *Brunner and Suddarth's textbook of medical-surgical nursing* (7th ed.). Philadelphia: Lippincott.

Smith, S. (1992). *Communications in nursing: Communicating assertively and responsibly in nursing* (2nd ed.). Toronto: Mosby.

Spencer, R. T., Nicholds, L. W., Lipton, G. B., Henderson, H. S., & West, F. M. (1993). *Clinical pharmacology and nursing management* (4th ed.). Philadelphia: Lippincott.

Stanhope, M., & Lancaster, J. (1992). *Community health nursing: Process and practice for promoting health* (3rd ed.). Toronto: Mosby.

Stuart, G. W., & Sundeen, S. J. (1991). *Principles and practice of psychiatric nursing* (4th ed.). Toronto: Mosby.

Taylor, C., Lillis, C., & LeMone, P. (1993). *Fundamentals of nursing: The art and science of nursing care* (2nd ed.). Philadelphia: Lippincott.

Timby, B. K., & Lewis, L. W. (1992). *Fundamental skills and concepts in patient care* (5th ed.). Philadelphia: Lippincott.

Whaley, L. F., & Wong, D. L. (1993). *Whaley & Wong's essentials of pediatric nursing* (4th ed.). Toronto: Mosby.

Wilson, H. S., & Kneisl, C. R. (1992). *Psychiatric nursing* (4th ed.). Redwood City, CA: Addison-Wesley.

Yeo, M. (1991). *Concepts and cases in nursing ethics.* Peterborough, ON: Broadview.

ADDITIONAL MATERIALS

PERFORMANCE PROFILE TALLY SHEET

TABLE A: COMPETENCY CATEGORY

CATEGORY	TOTAL INCORRECT				% INCORRECT
DC		÷ 19	X	100 =	%
AI		÷ 17	X	100 =	%
PC		÷ 20	X	100 =	%
IM		÷ 128	X	100 =	%
EV		÷ 14	X	100 =	%
CC		÷ 8	X	100 =	%
PP		÷ 52	X	100 =	%

TABLE B: NURSING PRACTICE

CATEGORY	TOTAL INCORRECT				% INCORRECT
PN		÷ 46	X	100 =	%
PsN		÷ 18	X	100 =	%
SD		÷ 26	X	100 =	%
CT		÷ 38	X	100 =	%
PH		÷ 34	X	100 =	%
CO		÷ 35	X	100 =	%
PR		÷ 61	X	100 =	%

COMPETENCY CATEGORIES

DC – Data Collection
AI – Analysis and Interpretation of Data
PC – Planning Care
IM – Implementation
EV – Evaluation
CC – Collaboration and Coordination
PP – Professional Practice

NURSING PRACTICE

PN – Physiological Needs
PsN – Psychosocial Needs
SD – Screening and Diagnosis
CT – Clinical Techniques
PH – Pharmacology
CO – Communication
PR – Professional Responsibilities

PERFORMANCE PROFILE CHART

TABLE A: COMPETENCY CATEGORY

% OF INCORRECT ANSWERS

%	0	5	10	15	20	25	30	35	40	45	50	55	60	65	70	75	80	85	90	95
DC																				
AI																				
PC																				
IM																				
EV																				
CC																				
PP																				

TABLE B: NURSING PRACTICE

% OF INCORRECT ANSWERS

%	0	5	10	15	20	25	30	35	40	45	50	55	60	65	70	75	80	85	90	95
PN																				
PsN																				
SD																				
CT																				
PH																				
CO																				
PR																				

COMPETENCY CATEGORIES

DC – Data Collection
AI – Analysis and Interpretation of Data
PC – Planning Care
IM – Implementation
EV – Evaluation
CC – Collaboration and Coordination
PP – Professional Practice

NURSING PRACTICE

PN – Physiological Needs
PsN – Psychosocial Needs
SD – Screening and Diagnosis
CT – Clinical Techniques
PH – Pharmacology
CO – Communication
PR – Professional Responsibilities

ANSWER SHEET
(See instructions on reverse)

FEUILLE-RÉPONSES
(Voir les instructions au verso)

Family Name - Nom de famille

First Name - Prénom

Date of Birth - Date de naissance

Date of Writing - Date de l'examen

/ /

DY - JR   MO   YR - AN

/ /

DY - JR   MO   YR - AN

Test - Examen

Fill in the information below **only** if you do not have a candidate label or if the candidate label is incorrect.

Noircissez les ovales ci-dessous **seulement** si vous n'avez pas d'autocollant ou si l'autocollant est incorrect.

Language of Writing – Langue	
English ○	Français ○

Place CANDIDATE LABEL here.

Apposer l'AUTOCOLLANT DU CANDIDAT id.

Test Form / Formulaire

Print and fill in the test form number

Inscrivez le numéro du formulaire de l'examen et noircissez les ovales correspondants

Candidate Number / Numéro d'identité

Writing Centre Code / Code du centre

1 ① ② ③ ④   31 ① ② ③ ④   61 ① ② ③ ④   91 ① ② ③ ④   121 ① ② ③ ④   151 ① ② ③ ④
2 ① ② ③ ④   32 ① ② ③ ④   62 ① ② ③ ④   92 ① ② ③ ④   122 ① ② ③ ④   152 ① ② ③ ④
3 ① ② ③ ④   33 ① ② ③ ④   63 ① ② ③ ④   93 ① ② ③ ④   123 ① ② ③ ④   153 ① ② ③ ④
4 ① ② ③ ④   34 ① ② ③ ④   64 ① ② ③ ④   94 ① ② ③ ④   124 ① ② ③ ④   154 ① ② ③ ④
5 ① ② ③ ④   35 ① ② ③ ④   65 ① ② ③ ④   95 ① ② ③ ④   125 ① ② ③ ④   155 ① ② ③ ④
6 ① ② ③ ④   36 ① ② ③ ④   66 ① ② ③ ④   96 ① ② ③ ④   126 ① ② ③ ④   156 ① ② ③ ④
7 ① ② ③ ④   37 ① ② ③ ④   67 ① ② ③ ④   97 ① ② ③ ④   127 ① ② ③ ④   157 ① ② ③ ④
8 ① ② ③ ④   38 ① ② ③ ④   68 ① ② ③ ④   98 ① ② ③ ④   128 ① ② ③ ④   158 ① ② ③ ④
9 ① ② ③ ④   39 ① ② ③ ④   69 ① ② ③ ④   99 ① ② ③ ④   129 ① ② ③ ④   159 ① ② ③ ④
10 ① ② ③ ④   40 ① ② ③ ④   70 ① ② ③ ④   100 ① ② ③ ④   130 ① ② ③ ④   160 ① ② ③ ④
11 ① ② ③ ④   41 ① ② ③ ④   71 ① ② ③ ④   101 ① ② ③ ④   131 ① ② ③ ④   161 ① ② ③ ④
12 ① ② ③ ④   42 ① ② ③ ④   72 ① ② ③ ④   102 ① ② ③ ④   132 ① ② ③ ④   162 ① ② ③ ④
13 ① ② ③ ④   43 ① ② ③ ④   73 ① ② ③ ④   103 ① ② ③ ④   133 ① ② ③ ④   163 ① ② ③ ④
14 ① ② ③ ④   44 ① ② ③ ④   74 ① ② ③ ④   104 ① ② ③ ④   134 ① ② ③ ④   164 ① ② ③ ④
15 ① ② ③ ④   45 ① ② ③ ④   75 ① ② ③ ④   105 ① ② ③ ④   135 ① ② ③ ④   165 ① ② ③ ④
16 ① ② ③ ④   46 ① ② ③ ④   76 ① ② ③ ④   106 ① ② ③ ④   136 ① ② ③ ④   166 ① ② ③ ④
17 ① ② ③ ④   47 ① ② ③ ④   77 ① ② ③ ④   107 ① ② ③ ④   137 ① ② ③ ④   167 ① ② ③ ④
18 ① ② ③ ④   48 ① ② ③ ④   78 ① ② ③ ④   108 ① ② ③ ④   138 ① ② ③ ④   168 ① ② ③ ④
19 ① ② ③ ④   49 ① ② ③ ④   79 ① ② ③ ④   109 ① ② ③ ④   139 ① ② ③ ④   169 ① ② ③ ④
20 ① ② ③ ④   50 ① ② ③ ④   80 ① ② ③ ④   110 ① ② ③ ④   140 ① ② ③ ④   170 ① ② ③ ④
21 ① ② ③ ④   51 ① ② ③ ④   81 ① ② ③ ④   111 ① ② ③ ④   141 ① ② ③ ④   171 ① ② ③ ④
22 ① ② ③ ④   52 ① ② ③ ④   82 ① ② ③ ④   112 ① ② ③ ④   142 ① ② ③ ④   172 ① ② ③ ④
23 ① ② ③ ④   53 ① ② ③ ④   83 ① ② ③ ④   113 ① ② ③ ④   143 ① ② ③ ④   173 ① ② ③ ④
24 ① ② ③ ④   54 ① ② ③ ④   84 ① ② ③ ④   114 ① ② ③ ④   144 ① ② ③ ④   174 ① ② ③ ④
25 ① ② ③ ④   55 ① ② ③ ④   85 ① ② ③ ④   115 ① ② ③ ④   145 ① ② ③ ④   175 ① ② ③ ④
26 ① ② ③ ④   56 ① ② ③ ④   86 ① ② ③ ④   116 ① ② ③ ④   146 ① ② ③ ④   176 ① ② ③ ④
27 ① ② ③ ④   57 ① ② ③ ④   87 ① ② ③ ④   117 ① ② ③ ④   147 ① ② ③ ④   177 ① ② ③ ④
28 ① ② ③ ④   58 ① ② ③ ④   88 ① ② ③ ④   118 ① ② ③ ④   148 ① ② ③ ④   178 ① ② ③ ④
29 ① ② ③ ④   59 ① ② ③ ④   89 ① ② ③ ④   119 ① ② ③ ④   149 ① ② ③ ④   179 ① ② ③ ④
30 ① ② ③ ④   60 ① ② ③ ④   90 ① ② ③ ④   120 ① ② ③ ④   150 ① ② ③ ④   180 ① ② ③ ④

INSTRUCTIONS

- Use black lead pencil only (HB).

- Do NOT use ink or ballpoint pens.

- Completely fill the ovals.

- N'utilisez qu'un crayon HB.

- Ne PAS utiliser de stylo.

- Noircissez les ovales complètement.

EXAMPLES/EXEMPLES

Right/Correct

Wrong/Incorrect

- Completely erase any answer you wish to change.

- Do NOT make any stray marks on the answer sheet.

- Do not fold or staple the answer sheet.

- Effacez complètement les réponses que vous voulez changer.

- Ne faites AUCUNE autre marque sur la feuille-réponses.

- Ne pas plier ou agrafer la feuille-réponses.

COMPLETE THE IDENTIFICATION PORTION OF YOUR ANSWER SHEET

- Print your name, date of birth, date of the examination and name of the examination (from the cover of your test booklet).

- Print and fill in the test form number (from the cover of your test booklet).

If you have a candidate label:
- Detach candidate label from your identification card.
- Place the candidate label on the answer sheet.
- It is not necessary to fill in the information to the right of the candidate label unless the candidate label is incorrect.

If you do not have a candidate label:
- Fill the oval corresponding to the language of writing.
- Print, in the appropriate boxes, your candidate number and writing centre code. Fill in the corresponding oval for each digit.

REMPLISSEZ LA PARTIE RENSEIGNEMENTS DE VOTRE FEUILLE-RÉPONSES

- Inscrivez votre nom, votre date de naissance, la date de l'examen et le nom de l'examen (apparaissant sur la page couverture de votre cahier d'examen).

- Inscrivez le numéro du formulaire de l'examen (apparaissant sur la page couverture de votre cahier d'examen) et noircissez les ovales correspondants.

Si vous avez un autocollant:
- Détachez l'autocollant de votre carte d'identité.
- Apposez l'autocollant dans l'espace réservé à cette fin sur la feuille-réponses.
- Il n'est pas nécessaire de remplir l'information à la droite de l'autocollant à moins que l'autocollant soit incorrect.

Si vous n'avez pas d'autocollant:
- Noircissez l'ovale correspondant à la langue de l'examen.
- Inscrivez, dans les espaces appropriés, le numéro d'identité et le code du centre d'examen. Noircissez l'ovale correspondant à chaque chiffre.

ANSWER SHEET
(See instructions on reverse)

FEUILLE-RÉPONSES
(Voir les instructions au verso)

Family Name - Nom de famille   First Name - Prénom

Date of Birth - Date de naissance   Date of Writing - Date de l'examen

/ /   / /

DY - JR   MO   YR - AN   DY - JR   MO   YR - AN

Test - Examen

Fill in the information below only if you do not have a candidate label or if the candidate label is incorrect.

Noircissez les ovales ci-dessous seulement si vous n'avez pas d'autocollant ou si l'autocollant est incorrect.

Place CANDIDATE LABEL here.

Appose l'AUTOCOLLANT DU CANDIDAT ici.

Language of Writing – Langue	
English ○	Français ○

Test Form Formulaire

Print and fill in the test form number

Inscrivez le numéro du formulaire de l'examen et noircissez les ovales correspondants

Candidate Number Numéro d'identité

Writing Centre Code Code du centre

① ① ① ① ① ①
② ② ② ② ② ②
③ ③ ③ ③ ③ ③
④ ④ ④ ④ ④ ④
⑤ ⑤ ⑤ ⑤ ⑤ ⑤
⑥ ⑥ ⑥ ⑥ ⑥ ⑥
⑦ ⑦ ⑦ ⑦ ⑦ ⑦
⑧ ⑧ ⑧ ⑧ ⑧ ⑧
⑨ ⑨ ⑨ ⑨ ⑨ ⑨
⓪ ⓪ ⓪ ⓪ ⓪ ⓪

1 ① ② ③ ④   31 ① ② ③ ④   61 ① ② ③ ④   91 ① ② ③ ④   121 ① ② ③ ④   151 ① ② ③ ④
2 ① ② ③ ④   32 ① ② ③ ④   62 ① ② ③ ④   92 ① ② ③ ④   122 ① ② ③ ④   152 ① ② ③ ④
3 ① ② ③ ④   33 ① ② ③ ④   63 ① ② ③ ④   93 ① ② ③ ④   123 ① ② ③ ④   153 ① ② ③ ④
4 ① ② ③ ④   34 ① ② ③ ④   64 ① ② ③ ④   94 ① ② ③ ④   124 ① ② ③ ④   154 ① ② ③ ④
5 ① ② ③ ④   35 ① ② ③ ④   65 ① ② ③ ④   95 ① ② ③ ④   125 ① ② ③ ④   155 ① ② ③ ④
6 ① ② ③ ④   36 ① ② ③ ④   66 ① ② ③ ④   96 ① ② ③ ④   126 ① ② ③ ④   156 ① ② ③ ④
7 ① ② ③ ④   37 ① ② ③ ④   67 ① ② ③ ④   97 ① ② ③ ④   127 ① ② ③ ④   157 ① ② ③ ④
8 ① ② ③ ④   38 ① ② ③ ④   68 ① ② ③ ④   98 ① ② ③ ④   128 ① ② ③ ④   158 ① ② ③ ④
9 ① ② ③ ④   39 ① ② ③ ④   69 ① ② ③ ④   99 ① ② ③ ④   129 ① ② ③ ④   159 ① ② ③ ④
10 ① ② ③ ④   40 ① ② ③ ④   70 ① ② ③ ④   100 ① ② ③ ④   130 ① ② ③ ④   160 ① ② ③ ④
11 ① ② ③ ④   41 ① ② ③ ④   71 ① ② ③ ④   101 ① ② ③ ④   131 ① ② ③ ④   161 ① ② ③ ④
12 ① ② ③ ④   42 ① ② ③ ④   72 ① ② ③ ④   102 ① ② ③ ④   132 ① ② ③ ④   162 ① ② ③ ④
13 ① ② ③ ④   43 ① ② ③ ④   73 ① ② ③ ④   103 ① ② ③ ④   133 ① ② ③ ④   163 ① ② ③ ④
14 ① ② ③ ④   44 ① ② ③ ④   74 ① ② ③ ④   104 ① ② ③ ④   134 ① ② ③ ④   164 ① ② ③ ④
15 ① ② ③ ④   45 ① ② ③ ④   75 ① ② ③ ④   105 ① ② ③ ④   135 ① ② ③ ④   165 ① ② ③ ④
16 ① ② ③ ④   46 ① ② ③ ④   76 ① ② ③ ④   106 ① ② ③ ④   136 ① ② ③ ④   166 ① ② ③ ④
17 ① ② ③ ④   47 ① ② ③ ④   77 ① ② ③ ④   107 ① ② ③ ④   137 ① ② ③ ④   167 ① ② ③ ④
18 ① ② ③ ④   48 ① ② ③ ④   78 ① ② ③ ④   108 ① ② ③ ④   138 ① ② ③ ④   168 ① ② ③ ④
19 ① ② ③ ④   49 ① ② ③ ④   79 ① ② ③ ④   109 ① ② ③ ④   139 ① ② ③ ④   169 ① ② ③ ④
20 ① ② ③ ④   50 ① ② ③ ④   80 ① ② ③ ④   110 ① ② ③ ④   140 ① ② ③ ④   170 ① ② ③ ④
21 ① ② ③ ④   51 ① ② ③ ④   81 ① ② ③ ④   111 ① ② ③ ④   141 ① ② ③ ④   171 ① ② ③ ④
22 ① ② ③ ④   52 ① ② ③ ④   82 ① ② ③ ④   112 ① ② ③ ④   142 ① ② ③ ④   172 ① ② ③ ④
23 ① ② ③ ④   53 ① ② ③ ④   83 ① ② ③ ④   113 ① ② ③ ④   143 ① ② ③ ④   173 ① ② ③ ④
24 ① ② ③ ④   54 ① ② ③ ④   84 ① ② ③ ④   114 ① ② ③ ④   144 ① ② ③ ④   174 ① ② ③ ④
25 ① ② ③ ④   55 ① ② ③ ④   85 ① ② ③ ④   115 ① ② ③ ④   145 ① ② ③ ④   175 ① ② ③ ④
26 ① ② ③ ④   56 ① ② ③ ④   86 ① ② ③ ④   116 ① ② ③ ④   146 ① ② ③ ④   176 ① ② ③ ④
27 ① ② ③ ④   57 ① ② ③ ④   87 ① ② ③ ④   117 ① ② ③ ④   147 ① ② ③ ④   177 ① ② ③ ④
28 ① ② ③ ④   58 ① ② ③ ④   88 ① ② ③ ④   118 ① ② ③ ④   148 ① ② ③ ④   178 ① ② ③ ④
29 ① ② ③ ④   59 ① ② ③ ④   89 ① ② ③ ④   119 ① ② ③ ④   149 ① ② ③ ④   179 ① ② ③ ④
30 ① ② ③ ④   60 ① ② ③ ④   90 ① ② ③ ④   120 ① ② ③ ④   150 ① ② ③ ④   180 ① ② ③ ④

INSTRUCTIONS

- Use black lead pencil only (HB).

- Do NOT use ink or ballpoint pens.

- Completely fill the ovals.

- N'utilisez qu'un crayon HB.

- Ne PAS utiliser de stylo.

- Noircissez les ovales complètement.

EXAMPLES/EXEMPLES

Right/Correct

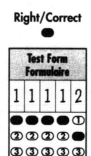

Wrong/Incorrect

- Completely erase any answer you wish to change.

- Do NOT make any stray marks on the answer sheet.

- Do not fold or staple the answer sheet.

- Effacez complètement les réponses que vous voulez changer.

- Ne faites AUCUNE autre marque sur la feuille-réponses.

- Ne pas plier ou agrafer la feuille-réponses.

COMPLETE THE IDENTIFICATION PORTION OF YOUR ANSWER SHEET

- Print your name, date of birth, date of the examination and name of the examination (from the cover of your test booklet).

- Print and fill in the test form number (from the cover of your test booklet).

If you have a candidate label:
- Detach candidate label from your identification card.
- Place the candidate label on the answer sheet.
- It is <u>not</u> necessary to fill in the information to the right of the candidate label unless the candidate label is incorrect.

If you do <u>not</u> have a candidate label:
- Fill the oval corresponding to the language of writing.
- Print, in the appropriate boxes, your candidate number and writing centre code. Fill in the corresponding oval for each digit.

REMPLISSEZ LA PARTIE RENSEIGNEMENTS DE VOTRE FEUILLE-RÉPONSES

- Inscrivez votre nom, votre date de naissance, la date de l'examen et le nom de l'examen (apparaissant sur la page couverture de votre cahier d'examen).

- Inscrivez le numéro du formulaire de l'examen (apparaissant sur la page couverture de votre cahier d'examen) et noircissez les ovales correspondants.

Si vous avez un autocollant:
- Détachez l'autocollant de votre carte d'identité.
- Apposez l'autocollant dans l'espace réservé à cette fin sur la feuille-réponses.
- Il n'est <u>pas</u> nécessaire de remplir l'information à la droite de l'autocollant à moins que l'autocollant soit incorrect.

Si vous <u>n'avez pas</u> d'autocollant:
- Noircissez l'ovale correspondant à la langue de l'examen.
- Inscrivez, dans les espaces appropriés, le numéro d'identité et le code du centre d'examen. Noircissez l'ovale correspondant à chaque chiffre.

SATISFACTION SURVEY

Your opinion is important to help us improve future editions of the *Canadian RN Exam Prep Guide* and to better meet the needs of nursing students. Please complete the following questionnaire, and mail or fax to the Canadian Nurses Association (see address and fax number at bottom of page 2). Your responses will be treated with complete confidentiality. Please fill in the circle corresponding to your response.

A. *PREP GUIDE* CONTENT

Please rate the following aspects of the *Prep Guide* content:

	Poor	Fair	Average	Good	Excellent
1. Background on the RN Exam	O	O	O	O	O
2. Test-taking strategies	O	O	O	O	O
3. Practice exam	O	O	O	O	O
4. Score interpretation of the practice exam	O	O	O	O	O
5. Performance profile	O	O	O	O	O
6. Answer rationales	O	O	O	O	O
7. Classification of questions (in Rationales and Performance Profile)	O	O	O	O	O
8. References	O	O	O	O	O
9. Overall content of the *Prep Guide*	O	O	O	O	O
10. Overall usefulness of the *Prep Guide* in helping you prepare for the RN Exam	O	O	O	O	O

COMMENTS / SUGGESTIONS: _____

_____

B. *PREP GUIDE* FORMAT

Please rate the following aspects of the *Prep Guide* format:

	Poor	Fair	Average	Good	Excellent
1. Overall size and length of the *Prep Guide*	O	O	O	O	O
2. Type of binding	O	O	O	O	O
3. Organization/layout of the *Prep Guide*	O	O	O	O	O

COMMENTS / SUGGESTIONS: _____

_____

C. *PREP GUIDE* MARKETING

1. How did you hear about the *Prep Guide*?

    ○ POSTER   ○ OTHER STUDENTS   ○ FLYER

    ○ ADVERTISEMENT   ○ NURSING INSTRUCTOR

    ○ OTHER: _____

2. Where did you purchase the *Prep Guide*?

    ○ SCHOOL BOOK STORE   ○ MAIL ORDER   ○ OTHER: _____

3. How much did you pay (not including taxes) for the *Prep Guide*?   ○ $39.95   ○ OTHER: _____

    Do you think this is reasonable?   ○ YES   ○ NO

4. Did you use any other exam practice book(s), in addition to the *Canadian RN Exam Prep Guide*?

    ○ YES   ○ NO

    If yes, which did you prefer?

    ○ CANADIAN RN EXAM PREP GUIDE   ○ OTHER (please specify): _____

5. What do you plan to do with your copy of the *Prep Guide* after you have written the RN Exam?

    ○ KEEP IT   ○ GIVE IT AWAY

    ○ SELL IT   ○ OTHER _____

6. Who are you?   ○ STUDENT   ○ TEACHER   ○ OTHER:

D. GENERAL COMMENTS

(Include any other services or products you feel would be beneficial to nursing students.)

_____

_____

_____

THANK YOU FOR COMPLETING THIS SURVEY.

Please send this completed survey by mail or by fax to:

Canadian Nurses Association
Testing Division
50 Driveway, Ottawa, ON K2P 1E2
FAX: (613) 237-3520